# Grasp the
# Nettle

# Grasp the Nettle

## Making biodynamic farming & gardening work

## PETER PROCTOR
### with GILLIAN COLE
### Illustrated by TANA LYONS

RANDOM HOUSE
NEW ZEALAND

A RANDOM HOUSE BOOK
published by
Random House New Zealand
18 Poland Road, Glenfield, Auckland, New Zealand
www.randomhouse.co.nz

First published 1997, reprinted 2000, 2002 (twice)

ISBN 1 86941 318 0

Printed in New Zealand by Publishing Press Ltd

# Contents

## LIST OF PLATES

# Foreword

 I feel special pleasure in writing a few lines to introduce this book and also to introduce the author. Peter Proctor leads an ordinary *grihastra* life surrounded by most of the worldly cares and responsibilities. He possesses a healthy body with an absolutely unassuming exterior. He has wedded spirituality to environmental and ecological farming.

His mission at this age of 68 years is to enlighten and train the farming communities, especially the youth of east and west alike. Peter has worked hard to promote biodynamic agriculture in Asian countries since 1993, and I feel he is having tremendous success in his endeavours.

I was given training in biodynamic agriculture by Peter in Hawke's Bay in New Zealand in 1993, and since then I have worked with him and his colleagues in New Zealand, Australia, Bangladesh and India, to popularise biodynamic farming. Now Peter has adopted India as his second home and spends two to three months a year in India, from south to north, from the Arabian Sea coast to the great Himalayas.

His role as teacher is important — it can never be over-emphasised that it is the efficacy of the system and the calibre of the *guru* or teacher that count, and a mistake in the selection of these may render all effort in vain.

*Grasp the Nettle* is a treatise on the biodynamic agriculture system, and it deserves to be studied with close attention by those interested in spiritual, sustainable farming or *ahimsak kheti* (non-violent agriculture). One of the main objectives of biodynamics is to realise the truth depicted in the natural farming of the ancient sages and Veda, Upanishad and other scriptures of the Indian subcontinent.

To know the historical and philosophical background of a movement is to know something substantial about its validity and potential effectiveness as well as why it advocates what it does. Biodynamic agriculture or farming is an ecological, self-supporting farming system rather than an industrial or chemical approach to the production of food. It has no adverse environmental effects and it promotes soil enrichment, conservation and construction. Soil is viewed as a complex and living entity and is considered the prime capital and wealth of the farmer.

Dr Rudolf Steiner in 1924 described what is now known as biodynamic agriculture, a new way of thinking about the relationship of the earth and the soil to the forces of the cosmos. He pointed out how the health of the soil, plants, animals and human beings depends upon bringing nature into connection with the cosmic creative shaping forces.

This book *Grasp the Nettle* is an attempt to present this knowledge in a way that should help the practitioner make biodynamic farming and gardening work. The chapters on observation of plants and their forms can introduce the reader to many other ways of furthering his awareness of plant life on the farm.

He bases his knowledge on a lifetime of gardening and farming, and in particular working at the Hohepa Homes in Hawke's Bay. He has brought the biodynamic concepts to many many people, in temperate and in tropical countries.

This volume should be kept in the libraries of all those who are interested in practising 'holistic farming'.

I wish every success and a healthy long life to the author to serve the world in the twenty-first century.

TGK Menon
Rural Agricultural Education Coordinator
Indore
January 1997

# Preface

 I first made and used the biodynamic Preparation 500 on the Hohepa farm near Napier in 1966. Having been a student of Rudolf Steiner's work since the mid 1950s, I had learned about making 500 from Australian Robert Williams, who had been making it near Sydney since about 1938, and also from Alex Podolinsky. It is interesting to note that the first 500 in the southern hemisphere was made and applied by Bernard Crompton Smith in 1928 in Havelock North, New Zealand. Later the impulse was picked up by GB Winkfield who made all the preparations after a trip to Switzerland, and subsequently shared his expertise with Robert Williams who passed it back to farmers in New Zealand.

Many people were studying and working with biodynamics in the 1950s and later, and this has given a solid foundation to what is happening now in the late 1990s. It was all pretty new to us in New Zealand at that stage. However several people in Hawke's Bay at that time — John Donaldson, Gheit Wiersmar, Shirley Wall, Michael Jackson, and Shirley and Clifford Harmer — were noticing the change in soil structure and also the improvement in food quality after applying Preparation 500. In particular, John Donaldson was growing Sturmer apples, asparagus, poultry and pigs and Gheit Wiersmar concentrated on carrots and potatoes. These products were my family's introduction to the wonderful taste of biodynamically grown food.

In 1973 when the late Tom Stevens, a dairy farmer from Kaukapakapa, was encouraged by his daughter Ina to come to Hohepa and tasted the Hohepa Golden Delicious apples, he wanted to use 500 on his cow paddocks. Why? 'Because,' he said, 'if you can grow apples as sweet as that I could grow grass that's as sweet' — and he did!

Tom was at that point 72 years old. He had been dairy farming all his life and was considering retirement. But he equipped himself with a stirring machine and spray gear to apply the 500, and made a new start to his dairy farming. Tom was very impressed with the results he achieved, and loved showing people how his soil had improved.

Shortly after that, John Pearce and his wife Norrie, who as a child had been a neighbour of the Stevens, paid them a visit when looking for ways to manage the farm they had recently bought. They quickly saw the advantages of biodynamic farming, which they applied to their 400-acre sheep and beef farm at Shelly Beach on the Kaipara Harbour in Northland.

One of the initial results from both these farms, which was a surprise to everyone, was that there were no cases of facial eczema in the sheep or cattle on either of their farms during a severe outbreak in Northland in the late 1970s. This outstanding result in animal health prompted a brief MAF investigation, but at that stage biodynamics was perhaps a little bit radical for many scientists and farmers!

The pioneering work of these and other families in the early days was invaluable — it helped bring biodynamic management into commercial enterprises.

Peter Proctor
Havelock North
January 1997

# Introduction

*if thou knowest it not,*
*this dying and becoming*
*thou art a troubled guest*
*across the world a'roaming . . .*
— Goethe

One of the underlying principles of biodynamic farming is the developing of lifegiving humus out of dead organic material. This biologically active humus is the basis of all living soil.

Can you recognise a healthy soil? Can you tell if your plants are healthy? Farmers, sometimes unwittingly, have taken on the responsibility to heal the earth and produce food that heals human beings. But a farmer who walks thoughtfully over the land and harvests crops with reverence produces a different product from one who drives a combine harvester all day with the radio playing.

Biodynamic agriculture is a method of farming that aims to treat the farm as a living system which interacts with the environment, to build healthy, living soil and to produce food that nourishes and vitalises and helps to develop mankind. The underlying principle of biodynamics is making lifegiving compost out of dead material. The methods are derived from the teachings of Rudolf Steiner and subsequent practitioners.

Steiner built up his knowledge from keen observation of plant and animal forms and traditional peasant practice, scientific study and deep spiritual research. He gave his teaching on agriculture in the Agriculture Lectures in 1924, towards the end of his life.[1] By this time he had developed a high level of spiritual awareness. His gift to the world is knowledge from the spiritual world that enables people to

1   The recent translation of Steiner's *Agriculture* by CE Creeger and M Gardner includes the first translation from the German of Steiner's lecture notes: Steiner (1993), *Agriculture* (Bio-Dynamic Association, Kimberton, PA).

recreate and work with natural forces in the fields of education, medicine and agriculture. Steiner taught that 'Matter is never without Spirit, and Spirit never without Matter.'

## History of the movement

To understand biodynamic agriculture and its relevance for modern agriculture, it is a good idea to look at the background circumstances of Steiner's Agriculture Lectures, which he gave to a small group of farmers on a farm estate in Koberwitz, East Germany (now in the west of Poland, near the border with Austria).

In those days the conventional way of farming was what we would now call organic. Farmers did not use artificial fertilisers. They put all the dung from their overwintering barns back on the field, and along with growing soil-sustaining green crops and the sound use of crop rotation, they maintained a high soil fertility. However, even with good soil and animal husbandry, farmers found their crops were not doing as well as they should; seeds were not as viable, there was an increase in animal ill-health and food did not taste as good. Something needed to be done.

Farmers who knew of Rudolf Steiner's philosophy of spiritual science asked him if he could address these problems. Steiner pointed out that plants grew not only through the fertility of the soil, but also with support from the cosmos — the rhythms of the sun, moon, planets and the wider constellations of the zodiac. This cosmic support, he said, streams into the earth through the living nature of the soil and is important for the healthy growth and quality of the plants.

According to Steiner, as the earth becomes older the soil naturally becomes weaker and is less able to receive these cosmic rhythms than in previous times. He felt that a renewal in agriculture was necessary in order to find a way to re-enliven the earth so the cosmic energies could again stream strongly into the soil. He introduced the practice of making preparations based on cow manure, silica, and various herbal plants, to be used in order to open up the soil to these influences again. He also made plain the intimate connection between all living things and the cosmos, and the importance of learning the workings of the planets and the heavenly bodies.

## Significance for the present

Modern agriculture has tried to come to terms with this ageing of the earth with a chemical approach. To maintain the levels of crop production needed, and to control the accompanying diseases, farmers use massive applications of a whole arsenal of sophisticated chemicals. But this, as we can already see, is leading to an environmental disaster with the poisoning of the soil, water and air.

At the same time, a huge amount of money is being spent on research into the use of chemicals and into genetically engineering plants and animals to solve problems that are in large part manmade. But some modern agricultural scientists are unaware of the importance of the living quality of the soil for healthy growth.

Steiner advocated discontinuing the use of chemical fertilisers altogether. Because of their inherent lack of life, he felt, chemicals could not maintain life or increase fertility in the soil.

The answer to problems of human and animal health and degradation of our environment lies in maintaining a truly fertile soil, by practices such as crop rotations, incorporating plenty of organic matter and the biodynamic preparations as described in this book.

Farmers carry an enormous responsibility, not only in caring for the land but also in growing food which will be eaten by human beings, and which will give them life and vitality. The quality of the food we grow and eat is directly dependent on the cosmic energy that can come into a living soil, and this is what supports our daily life. According to Steiner, the life forces in our food influence the quality of our thinking and our interaction with other people.

Conscious thinking about and working with these cosmic formative forces, and applying this knowledge in making the biodynamic preparations, is what distinguishes biodynamic farming from organic farming and permaculture.

Biodynamic farmers and gardeners treat the farm as a unity, in the context of its ecological environment. They work to increase the cosmic formative forces that enhance plant and animal health and growth. It is important that they develop their powers of observation, since biodynamic management relies on working with the natural life processes in soil, plant and animals. Each farm or garden has its unique microenvironment, and the farmer or gardener cannot rely on following a prescribed management plan such as the spray calendars used in conventional farming.

*Grasp the Nettle* encourages readers to observe and think about the forms and patterns in nature. For example, the spiral or vortex is fundamental to plant life. Biodynamic practice uses this same movement in stirring the biodynamic preparations. Biodynamic farmers can apply the knowledge gained from such observations to solving practical problems such as weed and pest management.

This book provides information on how to make and apply the biodynamic preparations; the times in the planetary calendar for carrying out various tasks; weed and pest management; and converting farms, orchards and gardens to biodynamic management.

The biodynamic preparations referred to in the book, which are essential ingredients of biodynamic farm management, can often be purchased from biodynamic associations (listed in appendix 7). Thee associations can also provide advice about the Demeter standards required for certification as a biodynamic farm.

Biodynamic farmers try to work with the rhythms of the moon, planets and constellations. For an explanation of what is means in the book by such terms as 'descending phase of the moon' and 'an air/light day', please refer to the New Zealand BioDynamic Association's *BioDynamic Farming and Gardening Calendar*, or to Maria Thun, *Working on the Land and the Constellations*.

The potential importance of biodynamic farming is being realised in countries such as India, where groups of dedicated practitioners are learning how to adapt the same principles to their particular conditions. This book includes observations based on experience in countries other than New Zealand, particularly India, the United States and Europe.

Biodynamic farming is a new direction in agriculture that will benefit our planet in the future. I hope that this book will inspire all growers the world over to take up the challenge.

# ONE

# The spiral and its expression in nature — water, weather and plant forms

 Have you ever noticed that a hose pipe running down a paved path does not go in a straight line? It starts to move of itself — it meanders and spirals, and if you observe closely, you will see a pulsing movement. This pulsing is the beginning of the vortex.

The form of the vortex is manifested in many different ways in nature. Galaxies, for instance, move around in great spirals, and spiral movements are the basis of cyclones and anticyclones in weather systems. Observation of the connection of the vortex with life may help the understanding of biodynamic practices, such as the stirring of the preparations.

What happens in a vortex? There is a continuous, two-way rhythmical movement of water (or air), expanding and contracting. The water is moving at different speeds — slower at the edge and faster as it moves inwards and downwards and then up and out again. It is amazing that no particle of water is moving at the same speed as any other. In a large enough body of water the particles furthest from the vortex do not move at all and become still. In a running stream you can see all kinds of intricate swirling and vortices as the water moves in many different ways at once.

The intricacies of vortices in nature have been described by Theodor Schwenk in *Sensitive Chaos* (1965).

According to Schwenk, vortices are created when two streams of water move past each other at different speeds. A hollow develops, into which oxygen flows: 'Boundary surfaces, with their rhythmical processes are the birthplaces of living things.'

The association of the vortex with pulsing, the life-bringing process, is the basis of many biodynamic practices. Vortices are formed during hand-stirring of the preparations, liquid manure and cowpat pit. The Virbela flowform has been specially developed to induce spiral vortices in the flowing water as a method of stirring preparations.

When we recreate this vortex in biodynamic farming, we are connecting with the universal creative water rhythms or pulse within the body of the earth. This can be found in all living things, for example in the heartbeat (see chapter 4, 'Flowforms'). It is exciting to discover the expression of the vortex in spiral forms in nature.

## SPIRALS IN NATURE

*In water spouts and clouds*
Often on the coast in a windy bay, spiralling waterspouts can be seen moving dramatically across the sea. Tornadoes whirling across the land build up tremendous power. And if you stand on top of any part of the main New Zealand dividing range during a strong westerly airflow, you can observe the clouds spiralling high above as they blow in from the west.

The Meteorological Service of New Zealand has a speeded-up film made from satellite photos of weather patterns across the Tasman Sea. The film shows the high and low weather systems in inward- and outward-spiralling forms (cyclones and anticyclones), which look for all the world like a mighty river in turbulent flood.

*In rivers*
Any river, whether in flood or not, shows a pronounced turning, twisting, spiralling as it flows through gorge or over plain.

*In shells*
On the beach at the high-tide mark you can often pick up shells which show the varying, beautiful forms of the spiral — think, for example, of the nautilus or the turret shell. The large New Zealand bush snail also has a strikingly spiralled shell.

*Turret shell*

*In leaves*

One of the spirals best known to all New Zealanders is the majestic unfolding spiral of the ponga fern (*Dicksonia fibrosa*).

This spiralling can often be seen clearly if you look down on a plant stem and observe how the leaf nodes gently spiral in two directions. This is particularly noticeable in one of the biodynamic preparation plants, the stinging nettle, *Urtica dioica*. The same effect is dramatically shown in the tight leaf configuration of many conifers such as the silver spruce (*Abies pinsapo*), or the Australian bunyan pine (*Araucaria bidwillii*).

Further obvious spirals in nature can be seen in the growth habits of the climbing plants such as the clematis spp. and the New Zealand bush lawyer (*Rubus australis*). Kowhai leaves (*Sophora microphylla*) also unfold in a spiral motion.

Look at the spiral tendrils on pumpkin and cucumber plants and the spiral pattern in which brussels sprouts are arranged around the stem of the plant.

The spirally arranged scars on the stem of Phoenix palms (*Phoenix canariensis*) where the fronds have been discarded make it look for all the world like a great pineapple.

A spiral is made up of a series of halfmoon shapes — the form in which water expresses itself. This watery form can be seen mainly expressed in the leaves, but also in other parts of plants.

*Ponga fern*

*The spiral and its expression in nature*  17

*Pumpkin tendrils*

### In flowers

Have you noticed the wonderful patterns in the flowers of the Compositae (daisy) family? In the centre of a composite flower such as a chrysanthemum, marguerite daisy, sunflower or single calendula, all the small unopened buds form a two-way spiral.

What more beautiful than the spiralling expressed in the rose's tight bud? See how the petals exhibit this delicate beauty as the spiral unfolds around the base of the bud.

You can also observe spirals in many other flowers, such as the unopened buds of flax flowers, hollyhocks, convolvulus and campanulas. The heads of the Romanesque broccoli show double spiralling.

### In fruits

Various fruits are in the form of a spiral. The pinecone, for instance, actually spirals two ways — a long spiral and a short spiral of different lengths, going around the cone in opposite directions. Fruits such as pineapples, strawberries and raspberries show similar two-way spirals.

*Daisy*

*Kauri cone*

Consider the marvels of the pea family (Leguminosae), and the way the pods display many spiral forms as they explode to disperse their seeds. Sweet peas, broom and gorse have these very twisted pods; and peas, beans and sweet peas show this spiralling in the twisting stems of their tendril-like leaves.

With such a tapestry of spiralling forms in nature, can you appreciate the life-giving ability of the vortex? Try to imagine the formation of the plant as a dynamic flowing process of which the physical plant is the end result. What we see in the spiral plant form is the memory of the vortex 'frozen' into that form. Each plant expresses this water movement in a slightly different way.

*Lupin seedpod*

# TWO

# A closer look at plant forms

## ELEMENTS

Much of the basic form of plants, such as the shape of their leaves,  fruits and flowers, can be attributed to the action of four elements that we continually experience around us and take for granted. Life on earth is supported by warmth, air/light, water, and solidity. Because our world has always been part of us, and is so harmonious and perfect, we do not stop to think about the environment that supports it.

It is interesting to consider the stages of growth of a plant in relation to the elements. They fall into a logical progression: the roots are the most solid part; the green leaves are the watery part; the colour of the flowers is connected to the light; and the fruits and seeds are ripened by the warmth.

> Roots — Solidity
> Leaves — Water
> Flowers — Light
> Fruits — Warmth

These four elements have been studied by Rudolf Steiner and later by Guenther Wachsmuth in *The Etheric Formative Forces* (1932). Both Steiner and Wachsmuth described the characteristic forms they felt were typical of the four elements. To the cosmic energy force that supports life, Steiner gave the name 'etheric'; the force that holds and gives shape to plants he called the 'etheric formative force'. If we look at the typical shapes expressed by the elements, it is possible to see in which element a plant is living, and how these forms intermingle.

### Warmth

*Warmth* spreads out and diffuses everywhere. It has no form or solidity and we experience it only by feeling. It is either too much, too little or just right. Warmth is supportive.

Warmth is expressed by a sphere, typified in nature by the roundness of most fruits, for example pumpkin, apple, or bean seed. This
warmth element has been named *warmth ether*.

## Light

*Light* is also without form; it spreads over the earth and diffuses
everywhere. But we can see light — for example, in a flash of lightning or in the billowing flames of a bonfire — and we can see the lack
of it. Light is more dense than warmth. It is interesting to consider
each of these two elements separately — warmth without light, and
light without warmth.

Light and air show a triangulation, which can be seen in forked
lightning, or in light rays when you squint at a candle flame. The airy
light element has been named *light ether*.

## Water

*Water* is more dense and able to hold a shape briefly. It can be touched, it can run through one's fingers. Water has the ability to be mobile and continually changing. It goes through a whole transition of density, from airy mist to drops of rain to flowing rivers to mighty moving seas, and at the poles, solid ice. Within all these states of water on earth there is an amazing variety of forms

Water takes on a halfmoon form, indications of which are so often seen in the spiralling, meandering, wave-rolling forms of water. The name given to this element takes a little understanding. Because water supports organic chemical changes in the leaf of the plant, it has been given the name *chemical ether*. Another aspect of water is that it supports sound: when there is moisture in the air, sound from afar is carried and enhanced. This prompts the name of *tone* or *sound ether*.

## Solidity

The element of *solidity* is the one with which we are most familiar. It holds its shape, is fixed, and is the densest state of the four elements.

Solidity is perhaps best represented by the cube, which typifies the final condensation and is the densest of the ethers. The cube is the crystalline form exhibited by common salt, which is present in the roots of many food plants. The name given to this element is *life ether*, meaning that it is present in the solidity of the earth which gives life support to all living creatures. A typical solidification of ether is seen in tree trunks. The wood from which your table is made contains

material which has once borne water and is now dense and solid, hardened by life forces.

These ether forces give rise to plant forms of infinite variety.

## PLANTS AND THE ELEMENTS

The form of a plant provides an expression of the influences developing it and also supporting it during its present growth. At each point of growth there is a different type of form.

### Roots and stems: mineral/earth ether

Roots show a solid, earthy, mineral nature, which is associated with a high salt content. The cube form can be seen when the mineral nature extends up the stems, resulting in square stems such as in the Labiatae family (lavender and thyme). This square stem form is often found in plants with healing properties. Some plants, for example bananas and Red Delicious apples, even show an echo of this square form in their fruits.

*Native mint*

*A closer look at plant forms 23*

## Leaves: water/chemical ether

Leaves are essentially the watery part of the plant. A predominance of the watery nature results in a typical leaf form — the halfmoon or spiral or river-meander or wavy form. Most New Zealand native plants, for example the taupata (*Coprosma repens*), show this watery form in their oval-shaped leaves.

*Taupata*

This water activity in the leaves and stems also brings about chemical changes. The main substance manufactured through photosynthesis is starch, such as in the potato. Starch can be tranformed into a variety of other substances, such as cellulose, and various proteins that the plant needs. The process of photosynthesis through which plants build up carbohydrates and protein from carbon, hydrogen, oxygen, nitrogen and sulphur is a wonderful and essential creative chemical process.

Think of the chemical process involved in the range of essential oils made by plants. For example, many different plants, originating all over the world, produce the lemon scent — lemon verbena, lemon balm, lemon geranium, lemongrass, New Zealand lemonwood (tarata) as well as the citrus. What is the common factor that enables these plants to make this scent?

## Flowers: light/air ether

Compare the flowing, watery, oval leaf-form of most New Zealand native plants with the narrow, hard leaves of most Australian plants.

*24 A closer look at plant forms*

*Acacia*          *Wheat*

The leaves of the eucalypts, acacias and callistemon (bottlebrush) have a sharper, lighter, triangular nature. This expanding, light, airy activity is particularly associated with flower forms. See how the acacia leaves in the drawing seem about to extend into colourful flowers?

Have you noticed the triangular form of petals in a daisy flower? South African plants like the protea show a similar light nature. In India the harsh, brittle light has resulted in many leguminous plants with finely divided leaves like flower petals.

All the monocotyledon plants, including the grasses and grains, show a predominance of the light nature in their triangular forms. All the leaves of the grass family are in the form of an isosceles triangle. Wheat shows a combination of light, warmth and earthy nature in its round and triangular grains formed into the square-shaped ears.

You can expect that any plant showing the triangular form will respond well to application of the biodynamic Preparation 501 (see chapter 5). The silica crystals from which this preparation is made also have a triangular form, which connects them to the same light nature.

Carrots have a triangular form in both the leaves and the roots and respond well to 501. The light nature is so strongly connected to this plant that the colour, normally associated with flowers, extends right down into the darkness of the earth.

### Fruit: warmth ether

Now look at the round, expansive form of pumpkins. This roundness and their colour can be related to warmth. Fruit and seeds generally can be related to a warmth process. Seeds need warmth to germinate and the plant needs warmth to develop its seeds. This round form also extends to leaves, for instance in the nasturtium, and tropical plants such as the fruit salad plant (*Monstera deliciosa*).

It can be an exciting experience when you start to notice the incredible variety of plant forms. Some show a mixture of forms; for example the leek leaf shows a triangular, light-dominated leaf,

*Leek seed head*

while the seed head is a large sphere, typical of the warmth process. Each individual flower on this seed head is triangular, and so are the seeds.

The difference between the relative role of the various ethers in different countries can be seen in the flower, fruit and leaf forms. For instance in New Zealand where the climate is mild and with a high, well-distributed rainfall, the watery influences can be seen in the leaf forms and minimal flowers and fruits; the leafiness is predominant. But in Australia, where there is much more light and warmth, the triangular form and to a certain degree the rounded forms of fruits are predominant.

*Development of eucalyptus from
flower to gum nut*

For instance, observe the eucalypt flowers which show a triangular, light form. As they develop they receive more warmth and form rounded fruits. The eucalyptus gum nut is five-sided, with little triangles on top.

Most Australian tree fruits are hard and woody. By contrast, only one New Zealand conifer, the kauri (*Agathis australis*), forms a hard cone. The rest, the totara (*Podocarpus totara*), rimu (*Dacrydium cupressinum*) and matai (*Podocarpus spicatus*), develop seed on an open berry, reflecting the more watery New Zealand environment.

## PLANTS, NUMBERS AND PATTERNS[1]

If you compare the form of various plants you will see that they are generally regular, with different numbers of petals and leaflets. The

1 For further illustrations of plant forms see Grohmann, *The Plant* (1974).

*Patterns of three and six: (clockwise from right) hyacinth; native iris; daffodil*

lily family (Liliaceae) have a three and six formation, with three petals inside and three outside. Hyacinths, tulips and daffodils are similar.

The eucalypt family, too, shows a great regularity of numbers, particularly on the opening of the seed case. Different species can have three, four or five openings. The *Pinus* genus can have needles in bun-

*Patterns of five: (clockwise from right) manuka flower and seed capsule; creeping lawyer; rose*

dles of two, three and five, depending on species: eg Scots pine *Pinus sylvatica* has two and *Pinus radiata* has bundles of five. Flowers in the Rosaceae family, which includes roses, plums, blackberries, strawberries and the New Zealand native tataramoa (bush lawyer), typically have five petals.

Other plants such as cabbages and clematis have four petals in a

*Patterns of four: (clockwise from right) speedwell; fuchsia; clematis*

flower. Poppies have four petals but their fruit capsule is divided into sixteen (see Plate 2). The passionfruit flower shows a seven and ten formation. Could these regular numbers have a relationship to the mathematical laws exhibited by our planetary or zodiac systems?

If you cut an apple across the middle you can see a five-pointed star in the centre. Cut a thin slice and watch as it dries: you will see the outline of the blossom and stamens in the flesh. The fruit contains the memory of the various influences that gave the apple plant its different forms. There is a perfection, a repetition and continual activity in plants.

Have a look at some of the plants around you. What an amazing variety of plant forms there are! When you look at plant forms in this way, can you visualise the activity that has given them life? Can you guess the type of environment that they evolved in? Can you also see the progressive change in form of leaves and petals going from the bottom to the top of the plant stalk as the plant reaches different spheres of activity?

# THREE

# The living soil

An essential part of the art of farming is the observation of soil quality. When the biodynamic activity is right, soils of all types have a common look to them. They have a crumbly, nut structure, and the humus content gives a slippery feel when rubbed between finger and thumb. A coarse feel indicates a lack of humus. By running your finger down the length of the profile you can determine the depth to which the humus is in the soil.

On a biodynamic farm, as the years progress, you will find that the soil has this slippery feel to lower and lower depths. The roots also penetrate deeper and deeper. Earthworm castings are found deeper too — down to where the subsoil and topsoil meet. The earthworms work to mix the subsoil and topsoil where they adjoin, increasing the depth of the living topsoil layer each year. It is important to observe the degree of mixing of earthworm castings between the subsoil and the topsoil. A good soil on a dairy farm after a few years of Preparation 500 can have over 100 earthworms (*Aporrectodea caliginosa* and *Lumbricus terrestris*) in a cubic foot.

Another observation you can make is of the nodules on roots of white clover. On average in a conventionally managed soil they would extend about 2.5cm below the soil surface, but in a good biodynamic soil they can extend down 20cm.

A good biodynamic soil allows roots to penetrate widely, so that they are not cramped and all the root hairs have plenty of room. Observe also that the soil clings persistently to the root hairs. This does not happen in a non-biodynamic soil. In a soil that has been treated with water-soluble fertilisers the roots are contracted and turned in.

*Top: compost worm* (Eisenia foetida)
*Bottom: earthworm* (Aporrectodea
caliginosa)

32  *The living soil*

*A ponga shoot unfurling, showing spirals within spiral.*
Below: *Poppy seedcase showing 16 sections*

PLATE 1, previous page: *Preparation plants, clockwise from left: yarrow, chamomile, nettle, dandelion, valerian, equisetum, oak*

PLATE 2

*Improved pasture*

*Red clover grown for seed*

*Otane wheat*

PLATE 3

*Splendour apples*

*Reed avocados*

*Biodynamic home garden*

*Romney coloured sheep on biodynamic farm*

PLATE 4

## Roots in various soils

In trials conducted in the Agricultural College of Indore in India comparing the effect of biodynamic preparations with that of conventional fertiliser application, there were dramatic contrasts in root development in the different plots. The biodynamic plot showed root development deep into the soil, whereas in chemically treated plots the roots were mainly near the surface.

*Soya bean trial at Indore, India, comparing root growth under different growing conditions. From left to right: 1) 500 & FYM (farmyard manure); 2) 500 & FYM & BF (biofertiliser — cultured bacterial inoculants); 3) FYM only; 4) N20 P60 K20 & BF; 5) NPK 20 60 20 only. Note the increase in nodulation on roots grown in biodynamic soil.*

I have observed the roots under a biodynamic tangelo orchard in the Bay of Plenty, New Zealand, and also under the neighbouring tangelo orchards. The orchard on one side used conventional methods and that on the other side had not been managed at all. Under the orchard managed conventionally the roots were constricted and contracted and there was no soil clinging to the roots when dug up. Under the orchard where nothing had been done there was still a certain amount of root constriction. Under the biodynamic orchard, the roots had moved freely through the soil and the soil clung to the roots when they were dug up.

## Soil quality using biodynamic or conventional methods

When you walk on good soil, feel the 'softness' underfoot. When you go to take a soil sample, feel the ease with which the spade goes into the soil. In usual conditions (eg not in a drought) the spade will go easily into a good soil. Observe how quickly the grass recovers after a drought or a prolonged wet period. Recovery will be quicker, the better the condition of the soil.

The ability of the soil to absorb moisture is very important. This ability depends on whether there is a turf matt or thatch. If there is plenty of earthworm activity a turf matt does not build up and rainwater penetrates the soil better.

When I visited a farm in the South Island recently, they had had one inch of rain the previous night, after a three-week drought. We measured the distance that the water had penetrated — 40mm deep. We also looked at the soil on a neighbouring conventional farm and found no water penetration at all. The thatched turf had caused it all to run off.

Researchers at Massey University in New Zealand recently made several standard soil-quality measurements on soil from several pairs of neighbouring biodynamic and conventional farms. They measured such things as the bulk density of the soil — the lower the bulk density, the more easily roots can penetrate deeply; the carbon percentage, which is a measure of the amount of soil organic matter; the mineralisable nitrogen, which is the amount of nitrogen available to plants; and the respiration, which measures the amount of soil microbial activity (Reganold et al, 1993).

They found that the biodynamic soils were generally significantly superior to conventionally managed soils in regard to soil structure, friability, aeration and drainage, lower bulk density, higher organic matter content, soil respiration, and mineralisable nitrogen, more earthworms and a deeper topsoil layer.

Tests for water infiltration were carried out in a comparison between biodynamically and conventionally managed orchards in New Zealand. These tests measured how fast water soaked into the earth to be available for the tree roots, by pouring water inside large rings and measuring the speed at which the level went down. In the biodynamic orchards, water soaked away between two and four times as fast as in the conventional orchards.

The vitality and quality of soil can be improved by regular application of:
• Preparation 500
• compost made with Preparations 502–507
• liquid manures made with Preparations 502–507
• cowpat pit manure made with Preparations 502–507
and in addition by:

- turning in plant material such as green crops and straw
- not using chemical fertilisers and pesticides
- avoiding soil compaction by machinery or animals, particularly in wet weather
- keeping soil covered by pasture, crops or mulch
- not destroying the soil structure by poor farming practices such as excessive use of the rotary hoe or cultivation in unsuitable weather (too wet or too dry)
- fallowing the land by planting deep-rooting permanent pasture species or using green crops.

These practices will be described in more detail in the following chapters.

FOUR

# Making and using the biodynamic Preparation 500

Regular application of Preparation 500 (cowhorn dung) for two to three years gives soil the good characteristics discussed in chapter 3. Earthworm activity, porosity, activity of humus-forming bacteria, crumb structure, clover nodulation, and root penetration are all increased. The moisture-absorbing capacity of the soil can be increased over the years at least fourfold, and humus depth can extend down about 30cm. Soil pH rises up to a point which is conducive to the support of clover and earthworms in the range of 5.8 to 6.5, then stays at that level. The soil becomes able to allow the plants to express their natural characteristics. This improvement of the soil takes place whether it is clay, peat, sand, volcanic, or silty loam.

Preparation 500 is made by burying cowhorns filled with cow dung in the soil for six months during autumn and winter. Cow dung has the amazing ability to attract life such as earthworms to it. Next time you walk across a cow paddock, have a look at all the worms under a partially decomposed cowpat. The cow is an earthly creature with a very strong and thorough digestive process. Some of the forces generated during digestion remain in the dung. Here we are looking at all that emanates from inside the body of the cow — her essential cowness, which Steiner calls 'astrality'. Every farmer and gardener knows the value of animal manure, and in particular cow manure, in improving soil quality.

The value of the cowhorns, according to Steiner, comes from their ability to hold and ray back continually that animal nature or astrality into the digestive system. This obviously continues to enliven the digestion and resultant dung to a high degree. When the horns are removed from the cow, they still retain their holding and raying back capacity. This gives the horns the ability to absorb the life energies that are in the soil in the winter months during the decomposition of

*Cowhorns filled with Preparation 500*

the dung in the horn. Something of the soil life activity is then contained and concentrated in the manure.

For an indication that there are strong growth forces in the earth during the winter time, just look at the way new white rootlets form and grow on newly planted trees and shrubs. There is no leaf growth during the wintertime, but there is plenty of root growth (see Steiner 1993, p71).

When Preparation 500 is made it takes on the characteristics of the soil in which it is made. So if the horns are buried in peat soil, the 500 looks black and peaty, in sandy or volcanic soil it is lighter, and in heavy clay soil the 500 has a heavy texture. However, even though it looks different, the 500 still brings about the same beneficial change in whatever soil it is applied to.

Ideally, the 500 should be made in the area where it will be used. 500 is particularly effective if it is made from locally produced dung on the farm where it will be used, as the forces in each district are slightly different. In New Zealand most farmers use 500 that has been made in Hawke's Bay or Northland. However I have taken some Hawke's Bay 500 to India and it has worked well there, too, in respect to soil structure improvement. In Germany, all biodynamic farmers are required to make their own preparations. In the long term it will be preferable for all biodynamic farmers to do the same.

New Zealand biodynamic farmers and gardeners have been able to benefit from the preparations they can obtain from the BioDynamic Association, which has a quality control based on 20 years' experience. However, after three to four years of experience in biodynamic management, farmers are encouraged to make their own Preparation 500, at the same time keeping a strict appraisal of quality.

## MAKING YOUR OWN PREPARATION 500

To begin with this should be done under the guidance of an experienced practitioner or the local biodynamic farm advisor, to ensure that the quality is maintained during all parts of the operation. At any one point the process can go wrong. If you are in any doubt about the quality of your preparation, have it checked by the farm advisor or by your Biodynamic Association (see Appendix 7). If it is not good quality, throw it out and obtain some that is. Your land may not be ready yet. The soil may not be fertile enough or the position of the pit may not be right. Try again the next year.

The quality of Preparation 500 can be checked by chromatography, which gives a pictorial image of the strength of the forces present. Several factors contribute to the quality of the preparation, in particular the quality of the dung used and of the soil in which it is placed. Researchers into the science of biodynamics in Christchurch, New Zealand have built up an extensive body of experience in making and assessing chromatograph pictures of Preparation 500 (for a description of chromatography see Pfeiffer 1960).

The experienced biodynamic practitioner learns after a few years to assess the quality of the 500 by the smell, feel and look of it, which is probably the best quality test. Massey University Soil Department has done bacterial respiration tests on 500 which show it to be 15 times more active than soil and twice as active as earthworm castings (Van Stensil, 1994). The advice given below should enable you to make good 500 yourself.

### To make good quality 500
*The dung*
The dung must come from healthy cattle fed on pasture that has been grown using biodynamic methods. Every year of biodynamic man-

agement the dung quality improves and so also does the quality of 500 made from it. To make sure that the dung is of good quality, choose the best paddock on your farm, one that has a good mixture

*Healthy cows in a
healthy paddock*

of grasses and clovers and produces the best milk. Shut the paddock up for about one month, then put the cows on it for two days before the 500 is to be made. Collect the fresh dung from this paddock the day you fill the horns. The dung should be fairly firm, not sloppy.

*Soil quality*
It is recommended that horns be buried in a vegetable garden where there has been ongoing sustainable management with biodynamic compost, green manures and preparations of the highest biodynamic quality. It is important that the soil is well drained during winter. Soil quality can be deemed satisfactory if it will grow good winter cabbages or cauliflowers. If there is any doubt about the quality of the soil, then mix with about 50 per cent well-matured BD compost, for the soil that surrounds the horns.

*The cowhorns*
The cowhorns used should be as local as possible. In temperate climates the best 500 is made in medium-sized horns. The larger horns that cows grow in hot countries such as India are more suitable for making 500 for those countries.

Small to medium horns, no larger than 5cm in diameter, make the best 500 in New Zealand and other temperate countries. The best and most durable horns are from Jersey, Milking Shorthorn or Friesian cows. Heifer horns can be used but it is generally assumed that

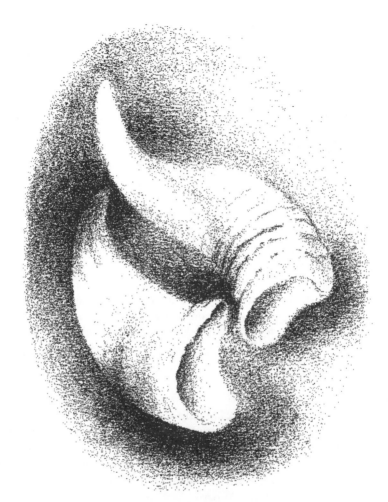

*Cowhorn and bullhorn: note the annular stress*
*rings and increased spiralling on the cowhorn*

mature cow horns would be stronger and contain more forces than heifer horns.

Use cowhorns rather than bullhorns. The cowhorn can be distinguished by having stress rings from calving, being solid at the tip, and being more spiralled.

Horns can be used for several years. Some last up to six years in New Zealand, but some become papery after one year. The durability varies with the breed of cow. If the 500 you make in a horn ends up green, ie the dung has not changed, it hasn't turned. You should throw that cowhorn away as it may have been used too often.

If the horns still contain a bony centre, put them in a compost heap so that the cartilage holding this centre part rots away; it can then be removed. This will take up to two weeks.

*The pit*
The pit should be within the fertile topsoil layer. The horns should not be buried too deep. In *Agriculture*, Steiner said to put the horns 75–150 cm down. This would probably be to keep the maturing dung in the horns out of the permafrost zone. In New Zealand, I have found that good results are obtained from digging the pit to 30–40cm. If your topsoil layer is thin, dig out some subsoil and backfill with topsoil from another part of the garden so that the horns can be surrounded with topsoil. The ideal size of the pit is 2 x 4m and up to 40cm deep.

## Method

To make the 500, fill the cowhorns with the dung and place them in the pit previously dug in the soil. In New Zealand and India the filled horns are generally placed open end down, to prevent them from becoming saturated with water in the winter. In Australia, where the winters are drier, the horns are generally placed on their side. The positioning depends mainly on the climatic conditions — there is no hard and fast rule. You can lay them on their side so long as you know they won't be flooded with water. Make sure the area in which you are burying the cowhorns has good winter drainage, where

*Burying horns in a pit, with marker stake*

*Making and using Preparation 500  41*

the water table is not high. On the other hand, do not choose a pit site that is sandy and dry. In a very dry climate you may even have to water the pit.

Allow space around each horn — they should not rest against each other, although they can touch at the tips.

When all the horns are in, fill the pit with soil, but gently — don't throw large clods of soil on the horns that might knock them over!

### Worms, weeds and wisdom

There are several things that can go wrong in the making of 500. Worms can be a big problem. In a biologically active soil the earthworms will be active and looking for food. There is nothing more frustrating than digging up the pit to find two thirds of the 500 gone. One year, out of 5000 horns buried, 200 had been completely emptied out by the worms when dug up. To encourage the worms not to work in the horns, put a few barrowloads of raw compost on the top of the pit as a lure.

A further point to note regarding worms is that they may be active during the time that the horns are in the ground. Horns should not be left in the ground longer than six months; in hot countries, check the 500 about four months after burying. In other countries, check in early spring to see if it has turned and to make sure the worms are not causing a problem.

Also, watch that weeds or tree roots don't grow into the dung in the horns. The root growth of weeds and trees is very fast in the early spring. Always keep the 500 pit free of weeds and grasses so that roots will not grow into the manure in the horns.

### Time to bury the horns

The horns are generally buried around October in the northern hemisphere, and around April/May in the southern hemisphere. The quality of the 500 might be lower if they are put in later than this. They can then be dug up again in April/May in the northern hemisphere or September/October in the southern hemisphere, which would mean they have spent approximately six months in the ground. See Appendix 3 page 162.

You may need to dig the horns up earlier than this if the soil is getting dry; for instance, in Hawke's Bay, New Zealand in 1994 the soil was getting so dry that the horns were dug up in September (early spring). If they had been left longer they would have lost quality. In wetter years they may have to be left longer for the preparation to have turned well.

The burying of cowhorns on a farm can be a social occasion for members of the farm, their neighbours and friends.

## Lifting the 500

When lifting the 500 in spring, observe the quality of the 500. If it is well turned, it should have decomposed and shrunk a bit. It should be slightly loose, so that it can be knocked out of the horn easily. When you break open the 500 it should have a characteristic sweet smell. You need to learn to recognise the smell of first-class 500. The 500 may take on physical aspects of the soil it is made in, but the smell is always the same. No suggestion of the cow-dung smell remains. After a time in storage the sweet smell changes to a very pleasant earthy smell.

Don't be concerned if the 500 has a small white or pink fungus growth or small insects on it. These are visible indications of the life processes.

*Digging up the cowhorns and emptying out the preparation*

## Using cow hooves, and other experiments

Rudolf Steiner pointed out in *Agriculture* (pp70–71) that the forces within the cow are rayed back into the digestive system by the hooves as well as the horns. I have experimented with putting dung in hooves. It certainly changed into something that looked like horn Preparation 500, but had a different, slightly stronger smell. This method will need to be well tested before it is recommended for use in mainstream biodynamic management.

Some farmers have experimented with new methods of making 500. Methods may need to vary to suit particular conditions, and it would be a pity to stifle ingenuity. However, the basic principles always apply. Any new method of making 500 would have to be proven conclusively before it could be accepted as a mainstream biodynamic method. If other containers or different dilutions are used, the 500 may be less effective.

## STORING OF PREPARATION 500

It is important that the 500 does not dry out as you are lifting it. Keep it under a damp sack all the time. The 500 loses its vitality if exposed to the sun's ultraviolet rays and the drying effects of wind. This can happen very quickly. To store the 500 for later use, place it in a glazed earthenware, glass or enamelled receptacle in a specially made peat-lined box and put it in a cool place, for example a cellar or coolshed. The lid should be loose-fitting to allow the preparation to breathe. Instead of being lined with peat, the box can be filled with loose peat or sphagnum moss; the receptacle, with a loose-fitting lid, is buried amongst the peat or moss. This method is suitable for storing all the preparations.

Don't forget to look at your 500 regularly, especially during the first two to three months. During this time the preparation undergoes a settling-down process as the biological life converts it into a homogeneous mass; ie the separate pieces of 500 cowhorn dung from out of the horns gradually form together. This is an aerobic process, which is why it is necessary to keep the 500 aerated. It should be kept damp, and if properly stored, should maintain a satisfactory moisture level; but if it seems dry, dampen it with a little rainwater and make sure it is compact enough, by gently pressing it together. If the 500 is getting soggy, gently move it with a garden fork to allow it to dry out a bit. The 500 is fairly self-regulating and it will absorb moisture if necessary when settled down. All the time you should be checking by smell to assess its state.

Well made and stored 500 should last for up to three years. As previously mentioned, it is important to make sure there is sufficient insulation around it. But don't store it in a plastic bag: chromatography has shown 500 stored in this way to have weakened in strength.

When the 500 settles down you'll notice some exudation, looking like small worm castings. A kind of black dust appears on the sides of the receptacle. This indicates that the 500 is now in a stable state. The settling-down process can take up to four months.

## APPLICATION OF PREPARATION 500

Preparation 500 should be made up to a solution with water before applying. Bear in mind that the preparation has to be stirred for one hour before applying. For the small garden, this can be done by hand.

### Water quality

Use warm rainwater where possible. The water should be warmed by the sun or a living flame, such as wood or gas, not by electricity. Don't use water containing chlorine or fluorine. If you use bore or spring water, check it's not contaminated, for example with iron, aluminium or calcium. If you have good quality bore or spring water, leave it in the air for a few days to enliven it prior to using, or run it over a Virbela flowform (see below) for an hour. Remember that bore water may not have seen the light of day for many years. Use a container that will not contaminate the water; an old copper is ideal.

### Stirring equipment and how to stir

Always dissolve the cowhorn dung into the water before starting to stir. It will mix quite easily.

For up to one acre of land you can use a bucket. Up to 14 litres can be comfortably stirred by hand with a small stick. Stir while resting your elbows on your knees. To make a good vortex requires a wristy movement. Start slowly at the edge of the bucket and move into the centre, increasing the stirring speed. When a crater appears in the water, break it by stirring in the opposite direction. You can change hands when changing direction, and it is easier to always stir outward, ie with the right hand clockwise and with the left hand anticlockwise. There should be about three direction changes a minute.

Up to 140 litres, to treat 1–10 acres of land, can be stirred using a 200-litre plastic drum or an oak barrel, with a 1.3–1.6m long, 2.5cm diameter wooden rod, suspended by means of a nylon cord tied to an overhanging branch or door beam. The rod is tied so that it is swinging 7.5cm above the bottom of the barrel. The rod thus tied takes all the weight and makes the stirring and creating of the vortex relatively easy.

For other stirring methods see Appendix 1.

### The stirring process

When you stir 500 into water you create lifegiving vortices and a pulse. After stirring for about 30 minutes, you may notice that the water becomes more slippery and viscous and easier to stir. The water has become enlivened by a similar process to that of the growing plant, the rhythm of the expansion to leaf and contraction to seed. In this process you have increased the oxygen content of the water. At the same time you have introduced the cosmic forces that enable the water to become a dynamic carrier of the life energy of the 500 as it is spread over the land.

A similar effect occurs whether the water is stirred in a bucket to form a vertical vortex, or whether a horizontal vor-

*Stirring the preparation in a 200-litre drum. The wooden stirring rod is slotted into a universal joint from the drive shaft of a Model T Ford*

tex is formed by passing the water through a Virbela flowform. This can be seen through the heartbeat-like pulsing that you can observe in both methods.

## Flowforms

*A flowform mixing Preparation 500*

About seven years ago at the New Zealand National Agricultural Field Days in Hamilton, the display of the New Zealand Bio-Dynamic Association featured a Virbela flowform, the Jaerna model. The flowform was working and we put in some cow-dung slurry from a local biodynamic farm as a demonstration of treatment of dairy shed effluent. We were flowing about 160 litres of water with 4 litres of cow dung, which was an approximation of shed effluent. We also added a set of compost Preparations 502–507.

The mixture became very frothy and gave off a typical cow-dung smell. About one hour after the preparations were added, the odour of the dung changed, becoming more sweet, and by the end of the day, about six hours later, the liquid was almost odourless. It ocurred to me that the movement of the water cascading down the

*John Wilkes, original designer of flowforms*

*Jaerna flowforms set up to mix Preparation 500 and liquid manure*

48  *Making and using Preparation 500*

*Virbela VB500 flowforms for mixing Preparation 500*
*and liquid manure*

flowform had had a marked effect on the working of the preparations. This phenomenon was repeated several times over the years,
with parallel trials determining the effect with and without the
preparations. Without the preparations the smell did not disappear
so quickly.

It was after this that the flowforms were used in New Zealand to
stir or mix Preparation 500. Farmers using the flowforms have
reported very good results, and I have seen the change in soil structure typical of the use of 500 which has happened with hand-stirring
or with machine-stirring.

I have pondered a long time over the connection with hand stirring, with the vortex formation and movement of water within the
Virbela flowform cascade. Having been a great observer of water
movement all my life, watching streams and rivers, the sea around
rocks and smooth beaches, I could see in the flowform a very obvious series of vortices formed as the water ran from bowl to bowl.

Also obvious was the pulsing of the water as it dropped into the
reservoir tank at the bottom of the cascade. It is almost at one with
the human heartbeat. Also one could observe the rhythmical varia-
tion of the water level within each bowl. Sometimes the water would
nearly spill over the edge of the bowl, sometimes it would appear
quite sluggish. I was reminded of the seventh-wave phenomenon of
the sea or the surging of a river around a rock, which is sometimes
covered and then exposed as the river flows by.

*Making and using Preparation 500   49*

But what of its connection to what Rudolf Steiner describes in *Agriculture* (p73) as the method of stirring 500 in a bucket and with the vortex?

Firstly I could relate that with hand-stirring in a bucket, the vortices in effect are built up vertically, one on top of another. In the flowform they are spread out horizontally on a sloping plane.

It was not until I watched an experiment on water phenomena by Rob Dewdney, a water researcher, who demonstrated stirring water in a glass jar and dropping one drop of black ink into the middle of the vortex, that I understood what was happening. The ink did not drop to the bottom or disperse through the liquid, but pulsed up and down, diffusing a little and looking like an archetypal jellyfish. Here was the connection between the two methods of water movement. The cosmic pulse! I could thus relate this pulse rhythm of the flowform to the world's great water rhythm, the rhythm of life, the cosmic pulse, the heartbeat of all living creatures, and so it appears to me entirely appropriate to use the flowform for the stirring of 500.

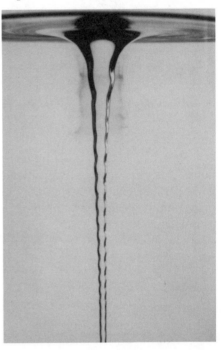

*Pulsing movement of water in a vortex created by stirring*

A large variety of flowforms now exist, allowing a farmer to stir up to 2500 litres of Preparation 500 in an hour — enough to keep an aircraft busy spreading it.

### Frequency, time and place of application

Preparation 500 should be applied at least twice a year — once in spring and once in autumn. The best application times are firstly in autumn, end August/mid September in the northern hemisphere, and March, April, or even May in warmer areas in the southern hemisphere. Apply again in the early spring (May/early June in the northern hemisphere; September/October in the southern hemisphere) or even later in cooler parts if it has been too wet or windy earlier on. It has been observed that 500 applied in the evening during a very dry spell helps plants to weather the drought.

Always apply 500 in a descending period of the moon rhythm. The New Zealand biodynamic farmer has found this time to be of great benefit in hastening a structure change in the soil. I have noticed that all soil processes are enhanced more quickly if the 500 is sprayed during the 14 days of the descent of the moon during its path across the ecliptic line. (If you are unfamiliar with these terms refer to the explanations in the New Zealand BioDynamic Association's *BioDynamic Farming and Gardening Calendar*, or Maria Thun, *Working on the Land*). There is an increase of rootlet development during transplanting of seedlings, a more reliable rooting of cuttings, an ease in the cultivation when working up a seedbed both on farm and garden, and a satisfactory harvest of root crops at this time.

Apply the Preparation 500 in the afternoon. 'Afternoon' varies at different times of the year: in early autumn it starts at around 4pm; in late autumn at around 1pm. Similarly in early spring after 2pm is suitable, but in late spring you should wait until 5pm. I always try to connect the application of the 500 with the inbreathing of the earth towards sunset when the dew falls.

The practice in Europe is to apply 500 only on bare land. However, New Zealand farmers have found that it is also effective when sprayed on grass — even on long grass. One farmer has found that light drizzle can be helpful when the grass is long.

### Quantities to use

The rate of application is 25g of preparation in 13 litres of water per acre, or 65g in 33 litres per hectare (see Appendix 1). This amount can be reduced proportionally for larger acreages, because of the radiating effect of the 500. A 1000-acre farm may require 12.5g in 13 litres of water per acre. All the preparation should be applied within one hour of stirring, so only mix up the amount you can apply in an hour. This amount depends on the method of application and whether you have friends to help spread the mixed 500.

Multiply the number of acres you can cover in an hour by 13 to find out how many litres of preparation to stir. For example, if you and your friends can walk over 7 acres of land in an hour, then the most preparation to stir at a time is 7 x 13 = 90 litres. If you can cover 50 acres per hour with a tractor and spray rig, then stir 50 x 13 = 650 litres at one time. Or if you are using an aircraft which can cover 200 acres in an hour, stir 200 x 13 = 2600 litres.

## Equipment and methods of distribution
After completion of the stirring the preparation should immediately be applied to the land. A larger area is easier if you have people to help. Use a good hearthbrush with natural fibres to apply the preparation over up to 10 acres. Plastic fibres are not satisfactory because they stick together. Walk rhythmically and throw every two steps, with a good tennis backhand stroke (not a golf swing!). A good throw should cover a 10-metre width. If you throw slightly up in the air, the preparation will spread out well. One person can cover one acre in one hour if they walk briskly.

You don't have to get a blanket covering of the preparation. The effect of the droplets of 500 will radiate out to some distance (50–200m) from where it has been consistently applied. One Northland farmer in New Zealand has never put preparations on one paddock in the middle of his farm, but the paddock is just as good as the surrounding ones where preparations have been applied, because of this spreading effect.

On larger areas, you can use a tractor or ute and a spray rig that will spray 20 metres wide. It is possible to cover up to 60 acres of rolling farm land using a 4WD utility truck equipped with a 800-litre

*Spray rig mounted on 4WD utility truck, including tank, motorised pump, and single nozzle; maximum coverage 60 acres/hour.*

52  *Making and using Preparation 500*

*Spray rig with single nozzle, 500 litres,
maximum coverage 40 acres/hour*

tank, $\frac{1}{2}$hp petrol motor, small centrifugal pump and a boom jet nozzle. Go round the circumference of a paddock, then zigzag across the middle.

It is very important to sieve or strain the 500 before spraying as the little particles of fibre in the liquid will block up the jets and cause annoying stoppages. Using pantyhose over the strainer is an effective way of eliminating blockages during the application.

Further details of different spraying methods, for example use of aircraft, are included in Appendix 1. Laborious as it may sound, there is wonderful satisfaction to be gained from making your own 500 on your own farm and seeing the results that accrue.

*Spray rig mounted on aircraft will cover 200 acres/hour*

*Making and using Preparation 500 53*

FIVE
# Making and using Preparation 501

 Preparation 501 is also made in cowhorns. The horns are filled with finely powdered quartz and are buried at the opposite time of the year from Preparation 500. The horns are in the earth between spring and autumn, the 'light' time of the year — between March and September/October in the northern hemisphere including India, and between September/October and March/April in the southern hemisphere. The action of 501 is a light process and it appears to me that the light forces are released from the crushed quartz crystals. The extra light is concentrated on the plants, increasing photosynthesis, strengthening the plant and encouraging the development of fruit and seed.

As Preparation 501 works mainly on the leaf activity of the plant, you should start using Preparation 500 first, to establish a structured soil that will support root development. Then after about one year of 500 use, start using 501 on your farm or garden also. Crops can be sprayed once or twice a year, during the growing season. The timing of the application for various crops is important. This is discussed below.

## Making the preparation

Preparation 501 is made by taking a well-formed clear quartz crystal (silicon dioxide) and crushing it in a metal structure or pounding it with a hammer or in a mortar and pestle made of iron or steel. Make sure the mortar and pestle have no rust on them. To keep them rust-free, wipe them during the year with a cloth impregnated with vegetable oil.

The crunched-up silica is now quite powdery and can be put between two sheets of plate glass to grind further, until the silica becomes 'mealy', with a consistency almost of talcum powder. It should feel smooth between the finger and thumb.

*Silica quartz crystal*

The powder is then made into a slurry with water, and placed in a cowhorn. The horn is left to stand overnight, so that the excess water rises to the top and can be poured off. The preparation will not fall out, as it would if it were dry. The horns are then buried in the same way as for Preparation 500. The horns are buried in spring about the same time as the 500 is dug up; in fact one could put them in the same pit. Choose a day when the moon is ascending, and not a day of a moon node. Don't forget to mark the site well with stakes and labels.

In autumn the horns are dug up and the 501 can be knocked out. It will be a bit drier than when it went into the horn. Expose it to sunlight to dry it out. Store the 501 in a clean glass jar on a sunny windowsill. 501 should always be connected to the light and thus never stored in the dark.

## Stirring and using 501

Stir the 501 using the vortex method in exactly the same way as for 500. For large areas it can be mixed in a flowform or stirring machine in similar quantities to the 500. The 501 is then sprayed in a fine mist using

*Making and using Preparation 501  55*

a knapsack sprayer, a tractor or 4WD utility vehicle spray rig with a similar nozzle as for the 500, only the pump pressure is 80–100psi. Always use warm water to spray with, as it absorbs the forces better.

You need 1g of Preparation 501 in 13 litres of warm rainwater for each acre. As with the 500, you are not aiming for a blanket spray. The best weather condition is a slight wind; avoid a strong wind. Aim for the mist to hover in the air for a time, then drift over the sprayed crop. It is nice to know that the spray won't have a harmful effect on the neighbours! Tall trees such as mangoes and bananas can be sprayed using a nozzle on the end of a wand.

### Time of application
Spray 501 only very early in the morning, at sunrise — usually in spring. 501 also can be sprayed during the summer, for example on a hay crop prior to cutting.

The 501 works on the photosynthesis process in the leaf. It strengthens the plant and the quality of the plant product. Because it is applied to the leaf, be careful that the concentrating of the sunlight does not burn the leaves. In most parts of New Zealand, where the

*Spraying Preparation 501 over mangoes, using a wand*

ozone layer is thin, you need to spray 501 early in the morning to avoid burning the leaves. This means that you should start stirring about one hour before sunrise. Some farmers spray at other times, but it's best to be very familiar with how it works before experimenting.

For maximum effect, the 501 should be applied at the beginning of a plant's life, at the four-leaf stage — in order to increase the bulk of the plant. Annual crops can then be sprayed again, just before harvest in the case of a leafy crop, or after flowering in the case of a fruiting crop.

*Fruits*
Fruit crops such as apples, peaches, plums and citrus are normally sprayed when the fruit is about the size of a shelled walnut. Some orchardists spray 501 each month, including just before bud movement and also after harvest, but not at flowering. Overspraying can sometimes make the skin of fruit or tomatoes tough. Every plant has its own particular requirements. Note: spraying fruit trees before the fruit has reached full size will cause premature ripening.

*Grains and hay*
If 501 is sprayed halfway through the plant's normal growth, it will tend to bring about a premature flowering, as the 501 very much enhances the light processes which are connected with flowering. This is why you should spray a wheat crop first at the four-leaf stage and a second time after flowering. Also, spray a hay crop just after it has been shut up for hay and then again after flowering, which would be a few days before cutting. Silage could be sprayed after shutting up the paddock and again a few days before the crop is ready to bring in.

*Vegetables*
Those who are familiar with the workings of the moon through the zodiac will know that spraying of 501 in an ascending period when the moon is in a particular constellation will impart the properties of that constellation to the crop. For example, to enhance a crop of broccoli or cabbage or even pasture, spray when the moon is in Cancer or Scorpio, which are water or leaf constellations. Spray a grain crop when the moon is in Leo, which is a warmth/seed formation period (see Maria Thun, *Working on the Land*.

Spraying 501 when the moon and Saturn are in opposition has been found to be very effective in bringing healing and strengthening qualities. The moon and Saturn are in opposition when they are

*Making and using Preparation 501  57*

on opposite sides of the earth. At this period there appears to be a strong balancing effect between the calcium and silica processes (see chapter 11). The 501 sprayed at this time enhances this healing, strengthening effect. In many cases, this has been found to strengthen the plants against specific fungus attack. There have been regular reports over the years of good results from spraying, for example, powdery mildew in tamarillos, brown rot in peaches, rust on oats, blight on glasshouse tomatoes, and mildew on courgette plants. One New Zealand farmer experimented with growing a courgette plant in a tunnel house and kept it growing and fruiting for 12 months without mildew by spraying monthly with 501 at moon/Saturn opposition.

Preparation 501 is very important for strengthening seed quality. Rudolf Steiner said that 501 would be of considerable benefit to the grains. I have found that spraying 501 on wheat, for instance, makes it very hard, with a high bran content; and it will change soft biscuit wheat into good quality bread wheat.

All the Gramineae family (grass and grains) show in their growth form, in leaf and ear, the typical triangular shape which is the expression of the light forces working within that species (see Wachsmuth 1932, and chapter 2 this book). This triangulation is expressed also in the quartz crystal, so one can assume there is a very strong connection between the Gramineae and silica. The high response of grains to 501 could be because of this connection to the light forces. All the Gramineae family are similarly affected, so hay also responds well. There is a sweet fragrance associated with hay sprayed with 501, and the taste of bread made from wheat that has been so sprayed indicates that the flowering processes have been enhanced.

The sugar content of grapes can be dramatically increased with 501. Sugar content is measured by the Brix level, which on average is about 25. In 1994, a New Zealand grape grower in Gisborne recorded a Brix level of 64 in his grapes, after they had been sprayed with 501. This is believed to be the highest level ever recorded in the world.

Care should be taken when spraying 501. It is a very powerful tool and should always be used with knowledge and experience. Hopefully what has been written here can provide a basis for further discoveries.

*SIX*

# Making compost, cowpat pits and liquid manures

## COMPOST

 Incorporation of well-made compost is important for maintaining and sustaining the humus content, micro-biological life, and earthworm activity of the soil. Compost has two uses: it is an immediate source of nutrients for a crop, and it is also a soil conditioner.

There are two stages to the composting process. First the pile heats up, and there is active and quick initial breakdown of protein with temperatures rising from 60° to 70°C. This lasts about six weeks. Stage 2 is a slower, stable humus formation, and includes worm activity.

Where immediate manuring of a heavy feeding crop is required, compost can be used before the earthworms have finished maturing it. For improvement or maintenance of soil structure — for example in a vineyard or on pasture — compost is better used in a mature state.

The aim in composting is decomposition with minimal loss of nutrients and the stimulation of beneficial soil organisms. It is not difficult but needs practice and observation.

### Materials

Two main types of materials used in compost are:

1 *Nitrogenous* — having high nitrogen content, and including fresh animal manures, fish wastes, green plant materials, kitchen wastes, blood and bonemeal. On their own these tend to putrefy.

2 *Carbonaceous* — more stable and having a high carbon content, and including hay, straw, shredded prunings, sawdust and other wood waste, dried seaweed, dried maize stalks, dead leaves.

Check your source carefully, as many of the above can be contaminated — for example, wood wastes by anti-sapstain treatments; crop wastes by herbicides; animal manures by drenches.

## Blending

The ideal is a homogeneous blend of carbonaceous and nitrogenous ingredients. In practice it is easier to alternate layers — for example layers of animal manures and fresh green materials interspersed with straw, wood chips, shredded wood and so on. A good idea in making any heap is to aim for 25 per cent animal manure content. If the manure is not available, make what you have into a slurry and water each layer with it. The layers of plant material should be 15–25cm thick and those of animal manure no more than 7cm.

## Moisture

This should be even throughout. If necessary, add water during construction — not after it has been built. Squeeze a handful of material — it should be like a moist sponge, where water can just be squeezed out.

## Air

An adequate but not excessive supply is essential to encourage aerobic bacteria. Too loose a heap, with too much air, will work vigorously for a short time, release ammonia and then become dry and inactive. Too firm a heap, with insufficient air, will smell putrid and sour — like the bottom of a swamp. An inverted V-shaped tunnel from layers of a hay bale or from tied bundles of twigs running the length of the heap will help bring in sufficient air.

The first layer should be made of hay or straw, but not too firm or compressed, as it would be if made from nitrogenous materials. Layers of loose, dry, stable manure create areas through which the essential micro-organisms and worms cannot penetrate, so these need to be moistened, consolidated and limited in thickness.

## Warmth

The optimum temperature results from the right balance of water, air and material. As the heat is produced primarily from the breakdown of the nitrogenous materials, too much of these will make it over-hot, causing nutrient loss to the air, or stopping the breakdown process.

Too much water and insufficient nitrogenous material makes for a cold heap that leaches out nutrients, while a dry one heats up for a short time and then becomes cold and inactive. The aim is heating up vigorously within two to three days and then gradual cooling over some weeks. Turning after about six weeks will restimulate the warmth process, but less intensely and for a shorter period of time. The heap should reach between 60° and 70°C.

## Size, shape and situation

The heap should be formed in a windrow not wider than two metres at the base and one and a half metres high. It may be as long as available material allows. Heaps of different dimensions can create problems: too big a heap can exclude air and the breakdown can be anaerobic; a heap that is too small will dry out.

*Compost windrows*

The site should be shaded from the wind and direct sunlight by trees such as silver birch, neem, alder, hazel, kowhai or New Zealand beech. Avoid trees with hungry roots such as macrocarpa, pine, acacia, willow or poplar. A permanent site will encourage build-up of desirable organisms in the soil beneath, so that they can move quickly into new heaps.

*Making compost, cowpat pits and liquid manure 61*

*Large-scale compost making*

The commercial farmer also needs to allow room to move machinery such as a front-end loader that will be used in making and spreading the compost.

## Minerals in the compost

*Lime:* Calcium hydroxide, also know as hydrated lime or slaked lime, should be sprinkled on any freshly cut green material or kitchen waste, as one puts sugar over porridge. Lime of any sort should not come into contact with animal manure as this leads to rapid breakdown and a loss of nitrogen. Hydrated lime is used in preference to agricultural lime because of its very active nature.

*Rock phosphate:* Where there is a deficiency of phosphorus, rock phosphate can be used in the heap. The bacterial action will help dissolve the phosphorus. It should be used at the rate of 100kg to 20 cubic metres of compost. Check the cadmium level: use a rock phosphate that has low cadmium — less than 20 parts per million.

## Other substances

*Blood and bone* or dried bone should be put through the compost heap rather than spread directly onto the soil.

*Rock dusts:* Depending on their nature these will, on breaking down into fine particles, add a clay content to the compost which will be beneficial to sandy soil.

*Seaweed meal* can be added to the compost at the rate of 25kg to 20 cubic metres.

## Biodynamic preparations

The biodynamic compost preparations are inserted into the heap at the rate of one set of Preparations 502–507 per 5 cubic metres (see chapter 7), bringing about an order and balance in the decomposition of the compost material. Likewise, when used on the soil, this compost will enable balanced plant growth. With good biodynamic compost we can add a much more varied and richer microbiological life to the soil, which can help combat many soil-borne pathogens.

## Covering

Some protection may be needed from the elements. In high rainfall areas cover the heap with something that will shed the rain: for instance, thatch made with straw or coconut leaves. Using black plastic or polythene is not advisable unless it is possible to allow the heap to breathe by draping it over a wooden frame.

In dry areas, build the heap in the shade and plaster it over with mud or cow manure, or cover with straw or large leaves such as coconut leaves to keep moisture in. Check the water content frequently and add more if necessary.

## Turning

The heap should be turned after about six weeks, and corrective measures taken if necessary — such as adding water if it has dried out. The turning process will bring the outside to the centre and vice versa, so an even breakdown will be achieved throughout.

## Rate of use

In a market garden, use $20m^3$ of finished compost per acre per year. On vineyards and orchards use at least $10m^3$ per acre. One cubic metre is a windrow 2m wide at the base, 1.5m high and 1m long, at the time of building.

COWPAT PIT

Manure from a cowpat pit — also called Maria Thun's barrel manure, as she first worked with this concept — is useful for spreading the influence of the compost preparations over a large area of land.

## Preparation

To make the pit, choose a site with good drainage, but one that won't dry out. Avoid the bottom of a hill or the dry top. A place in the vegetable garden is ideal.

Dig a hole 600mm by 1m by 150mm deep. Line the sides of the hole with bricks or a bottomless box of untreated timber, 300mm deep. The rim of the box will then stand 150mm above ground level. Backfill the soil around the exposed sides of the box.

To one barrowload (60kg) of firm cow manure, add 200g of crushed eggshells and 500g of basalt meal or dust, mixing thoroughly.

Fill the hole to a maximum depth of 250mm. Any deeper will delay the breakdown into humus.

Insert three sets of compost preparations 502–506 (see chapter 7), by pressing them into the manure to a depth of about 50mm. Stir three portions of valerian Preparation 507 for 5 minutes in 350ml of rainwater and sprinkle over the manure.

Cover the manure with hessian sacks to retain moisture, and then with a waterproof lid raised at one side to allow water to run off and air to circulate.

After a month, aerate with a garden fork, but leave the surface even so as not to cause excessive drying. If manure worms — *Eisenia foetida* (gold-banded lavender colour; see p32), *Dendronæria rubida* or *Lumbricus rubellus* (small red) are not already present, they can be introduced to aid the later stages of breakdown.

Depending on weather and temperature, the manure should be ready to use in approximately three months.

*Cowpat pits lined with bricks, under a shade house*

*Wrapping dandelion flowers in mesentery*

*Chamomile sausages*

*Barkla's effluent treatment*

PLATE 5

PLATE 6

Opposite page, top: *Tick bean and ryecorn grown as green manure. Middle: 2000l stainless steel tank containing liquid fish manure. Bottom: compost windrows.*

*Permanent brick-lined cowpat pits in southern India*

*Cleaning paint off cowhorns in India*

PLATE 7

*Plants grown under different conditions.* Left: *control;* centre: *using chemical fertilisers;* right: *in biodynamic soil*

*Two soil samples* — left: *original degraded soil;* right: *soil after two years of biodynamic farming*

PLATE 8

## Application

Cowpat pit manure can be:

• stirred with Preparation 500, at approximately 100g per portion of 500, as a way to spread the influence of the compost preparations over the land.

• used as an inoculant for dairyshed effluent, particularly where Virbela flowforms are being used. One kilogram will be enough for approximately one week's shed effluent from 100 cows.

• dissolved in water — at least 1kg in 45 litres per acre — as a liquid manure to be used on farm, orchard or market garden. Stir for 10 minutes before applying.


## LIQUID FISH MANURE

Fish waste can be made into a manure in a similar manner to other organic wastes. Sources of material vary from fish processing plants to game fishing clubs. It is also possible to combine recreation with work, and use the leftovers from the holiday fishing season.

Some biodynamic farmers make a surplus, and supply fish fertiliser to newcomers, who usually need it sooner than the seven months it takes to make.

A 200-litre tank of fish concentrate will do one application on 160–250 acres. For a bigger farm, you'll need bigger, non-corrosive vats — stainless steel, concrete or plastic water tanks. Make liquid fish manure in a similar way to other liquid manures, but add compost preparations twice, at the same rate — that is, one set per 200 litres (44 gallons) at the beginning, and one set per 200 litres about three months later.

Caution: Your family may not want to have much to do with you if you have been stirring the fish fertiliser — the smell can be very strong.

### Preparation

The method described below is one developed successfully by John Pearce, on his farm at South Head, Kaipara Harbour, on the west coast of New Zealand.

Use a 200–2000 litre non-corrosive container to dissolve the fish. Suitable containers may be old stainless steel milk vats, concrete water tanks, or even a plastic drum.

*Making compost, cowpat pits and liquid manure  65*

*Stainless steel liquid manure tanks containing fish and seaweed*

Before filling the tank with fish, it would be a good idea to set in place some form of filter inside the tank. This can be achieved using a length of perforated Novaflow plastic pipe, connected to the outlet on the inside of the tank and arranged into an upright position. This will sieve out the scales and bones from the broken-down liquid.

Fill with fish, any you can get. An excellent product has been achieved using shark and stingray, which have been sliced up or minced. However, fish heads and frames will also make a reasonable product. Cover the fish with rainwater and add Preparations 502–507. Add these in proportion: 10 sets for 2000 litres. Further preparations in the same proportions can also be added approximately three months later.

The brew can be regularly stirred after a month. At about three months it will be cloudy grey, but when ready to use, after about seven months, it is of a clear golden colour and the hydrogen sulphide smell has started to disperse. Note: it is a good idea to place the tanks well away from buildings because of this unpleasant sulphurous smell.

The use of Virbela flowforms, through which the fertiliser is circulated during the latter stages of the process, has been found to considerably enhance the breakdown. Pass the liquid through for 10 minutes before application.

## Application

Fish fertiliser made the biodynamic way can be applied at the rate of 1–2 litres in 45 litres (or 2–4 pints in 10 gallons) per acre. More concentrated, it may damage foliage. It can also be added to Preparation 500 towards the end of the stirring process.

This fertiliser can be applied at least three times a year and is very effective as a tonic on pasture, vegetables and fruit trees. It is a valuable source of trace elements; and to a certain extent, a stimulus in the nitrogen processes. Its use is also an excellent way of ensuring the full range of preparations are incorporated into the soil.

## LIQUID PLANT MANURE FROM SEAWEED AND WEEDS

Pfeiffer in *Soil Fertility, Renewal and Preservation* (1983) talks about plant dynamics, and how the predominant weed is able to supply the soil needs, particularly in degraded soils. In New Zealand, for example, thistle supplies copper and yarrow brings selenium. Seaweed liquid manure supplies a wide range of trace elements.

Liquid plant fertilisers act as a valuable tonic for pasture, vegetables and fruit trees. Use of these fertilisers is an excellent way of ensuring a full range of preparations are incorporated into the soil. They also boost trace elements and to a certain extent, potash.

### Preparation of seaweed

Use a 200-litre non-corrosive container to dissolve approximately 12kg of powdered seaweed or kelp. Fresh minced or ground-up seaweed is also suitable but should be used in a quantity to half fill the container before the addition of water. Use rainwater as this contains no mineral impurities which may inhibit the fermentation process.

Warm a quantity of water to 30°C to make the initial solution. This can be topped with cold rainwater. Add Preparations 502–507 as described for liquid fish manure (above). Stand the container in a warm place as this enhances fermentation. The liquid should be agitated at least once or twice a week for aeration and should be ready in approximately two months, when the liquid will be sweet-smelling and of a clear brown colour. It will be necessary to strain the liquid before using. It should also be noted that when the first liquid is taken off it will be possible to add more rainwater and dissolve more of the seaweed that has been left.

### Application

Apply at the rate of 15–30 litres in 270 litres per acre. This seaweed fertiliser can be applied at least three times a year.

## Weeds

Liquid plant manure can be made in the same way from weeds such as thistles, ragwort, or nettles. Shredded legume plants also make a good liquid fertiliser. Fill a drum with the weed and cover with water. Do not mix the weed species, as this seems to interfere with the breakdown.

# SEVEN

# Making and using compost Preparations 502–507 and Preparation 508

 Rudolf Steiner advised that all the compost Preparations 502–507 should be used in a compost heap. Each brings a particular activity. Some of these preparations take more time and trouble than does 500 but are very satisfying to make. A few New Zealand farmers make their own compost preparations. The main difficulties are in growing and collecting sufficient herbs and in getting the animal parts.

Whether you make your own preparations or buy them, continue to look after them carefully. Check the jars of preparations weekly. If one is drying out, add a very little rainwater. The yarrow preparation is one particularly likely to dry out. When picking and drying preparation flowers or foliage, it is important not to dry any of the different plants on the same tray.

The different preparations have different properties. For instance, the stag's bladder Preparation 502 is always loose and dry, while the chamomile Preparation 503 is generally humus-like but can become wet and tacky. You need to look at the compost preparations every day after digging them out, until they reach a stable state.

All these preparations should be made in a descending period of the moon, except for the valerian Preparation 507, for which the flowers and foliage are best gathered on an air/light day.

## PREPARATION 502 YARROW — Achillea millifolium

This preparation brings in light forces to the soil in the form of potassium and sulphur. Rudolf Steiner describes yarrow as a miracle of creation, particularly with its connection to sulphur and also to potassium.

*Yarrow*

The yarrow plant grows in waste places on poor soils. Yarrow plants are delicate-looking, but to my eye, beautifully balanced. The roots are mainly at the surface: they are not deeply attached to the earth. You can feel by the feathery lightness of the leaf how the yarrow is strongly connected to the light forces. The leaves have a reduced, flower-like gesture. Yarrow's main feature is its white, composite flowers, which are connected by light forces with Venus. Each flower is like a little chalice — a receptacle for receiving the beneficence of the cosmos.

This connection with the cosmic forces, one imagines, enables the yarrow to concentrate many trace elements. It is a wonderful example of what Pfeiffer (1983) has described as plant dynamics. Yarrow has been found to contain a measurable amount of potassium and selenium even when the soil in which it grows lacks these minerals. In 1985 in Reporoa, New Zealand, liquid manure was made from yarrow plants growing on land where soil tests had showed deficiency of potassium and total absence of selenium. Analysis showed the liquid manure to contain measurable amounts of these minerals.

The flowers are put into a stag's bladder — this can be obtained from a hunter or from a deer abattoir. The stag is particularly connected to the cosmos through its antlers and urinary system. If you look carefully at the stag's antlers, you can see that they have a form similar to that of the yarrow plant. Rudolf Steiner points out that the bladder is a reflection of the starry heavens (*Agriculture*, pp94–96).

## Making the preparation

If the yarrow does not flower early enough to use fresh, you will need to pick the flowers in summer or autumn and dry them for use the next spring. Simply cut the flower stalks and dry them on hessian racks, or tie and hang them up in bunches in an airy shed to dry.

*Filling stag's bladder with yarrow 502*

In the following spring fill the stag's bladder with the flowers which have been cut off the stems with a pair of scissors. If they are too dry, gather some fresh yarrow leaves and make them into a juice with a mortar and pestle and use this juice to moisten the flowers.

If the bladder is fresh and soft, it can be filled through the top using a funnel. A dried bladder can be moistened and also filled from the top. Alternatively, make a small slit in the bottom of the bladder and carefully put in the flowers, and then stitch up the slit. This is so that the bladder is 'waterproof', so it does not become waterlogged during any rain, which would

tend to make the
flowers go mouldy.
Do not fill the blad-
der too tight. Hang
the bladder in a tree,
on the sunny side,
well out of the reach
of dogs. The bladder
should be exposed to
the same weather
conditions as will
affect your farm dur-
ing spring and sum-
mer.

In the autumn
take the bladder
down and bury it in
soil of a similar qual-
ity and at the same
time as you bury the

*Stags' bladders hanging in a tree in summer*

cowhorns for Preparation 500. It is best to bury the bladder within a
small bottomless box surrounded with earth. The box is primarily
used as a marker, so that you remember where the preparation has
been buried.

In tropical countries, place the preparation in a large earthenware
pot and bury it in a brick-lined hole (termites will destroy wood).
Place soil in the pot to surround the preparation; it can then be recovered by knocking out the contents of the pot.

### Retrieving the preparation
When you dig up the preparation, the bladder will have rotted but
the yarrow flowers will still be there in a round brown ball. Lift it
carefully out and store it in a glass jar with a loose-fitting lid, and put
it in a storage box, as described for Preparation 500.

The yarrow preparation never actually forms into humus — you
can still see the structure of the flowers in it. As the nature of the 502
is quite loose, it can tend to dry out rather quickly. Press it down a little and firm it in the jar to maintain its moisture. If it does look a little dry you can always add a teaspoon or two of rainwater. Dry
preparations will lose their strength.

*Chamomile*

PREPARATION 503 CHAMOMILE — *Matricaria chamomilla*

This preparation promotes a good breakdown of the proteins in the compost to humic plant nutrients, and prevents the protein breaking down to ammonia which would be lost. It also brings calcium. The chamomile flower shows a delicate perfection of form.

Preparation 503 is made from the flowers of the German chamomile, not from the Roman or Italian chamomile (*Chamæmelum nobile*, or stinking mayweed, as it is also known). To check that you are growing the German version, cut open the cone on which the little yellow flowers are found. It should be hollow inside, whereas that of the Roman chamomile is solid. To grow your own chamomile, if there are none self-sown, you should sow the seeds in autumn and pick the flowers in early summer.

This plant is an annual and dies off after mid summer. It has a mercurial quality and tends to pop up in different places each year. Chamomile used to be used for preserving meat, well before the days of refrigerators; it prevents putrefaction by holding in the life forces. Chamomile is also used medicinally, particularly for digestion, and also for its calming effect.

## Picking the flowers
The chamomile flowers should be picked in the morning before 10am, when the flower petals are horizontal. In the very early morning while the dew is on them the petals hang downwards. The young flowers only should be picked — their centres are slightly pyramidal and greenish and they have a ring of pollen-bearing stamens at the base of the cone. When the cone is spherical and yellow, the flowers are too old to be of much value. You may find it easier to pick the flowers with a comb.

Drying the flowers is quite important. Spread out the freshly picked flowers on a hessian frame in a warm, shady, airy place (not in direct sunlight). Move them daily until they look dry. Then to dry them off completely, place them in a hot-water cupboard. If the little flowers have any moisture in them at all they will go mouldy in storage. Well-dried chamomile flowers have a beautiful fragrance. When they are crisp, store them in a brown paper bag or glass jar in an airy cupboard. Watch that mice or moths don't spoil them.

## Making the preparation
To make the preparation, you need fresh cow's intestines, which can be obtained from an abattoir or a home-kill butcher. Stuff the flowers inside them to make long sausages (see colour plate 5). I always use a wide-stemmed funnel to fill the intestine with the flowers. Cut the intestines into lengths of 25–40cm. Run them between forefinger and thumb to take out some of the partially digested contents. Then tie one end of the intestine. Pull the open end of the intestine over the funnel stem. Put a small amount of dried flowers into the funnel at a time, and poke the flowers into the intestine with a rounded wooden stick (eg the end of a wooden spoon). Do not pack the flowers too tight. When the intestine is full, tie the end with string. You will notice that any unpleasant smell associated with ageing intestines and warm weather quickly disappears when they come in contact with the chamomile flowers.

*Filling a chamomile sausage*

## Burying the preparation

The preparation should be buried in the autumn. To prevent dogs from digging up the preparation, you may have to put a barrier over the area.

The chamomile preparation is the most difficult to recover, as it breaks down completely and is not easy to locate. Earthworms are very attracted to chamomile and will incorporate it into the surrounding soil. I have lost much of this preparation over the years.

To enable you to recover the preparation easily in the spring, put the sausages in a large unglazed earthenware flower pot 30cm in diameter and bury the pot in the earth. You will have surrounded the sausages with soil within the flower pot. As the earthenware pot is unglazed, it will allow all the earth processes to travel through to the sausages. Alternatively you could put the sausages in a 'sandwich' of sphagnum moss in the soil and mark its position with pegs (see the making of the nettle preparation below).

## Retrieving the preparation

Lift it in early spring before any earthworms can remove it (they will also come into the flower pot). All the other preparations can be dug up in spring except the nettle, which is buried for 12 months.

## PREPARATION 504 STINGING NETTLE — *Urtica dioica*

Nettles show strength and uprightness and perfection of form. Their form, particularly that of the stings, is shaped by silica. The strength of the sting is an important indication of the value of the nettle in making Preparation 504.

According to Steiner the nettle is a plant with unique healing qualities for both humans and plants. If you sketch the nettle plant and draw a line to connect up the nodal points or the axils of each leaf

*Nettle*

you find the double spiral form of the spiritual staff of Mercury — the medical sign.

The forces of Mars that influence nettles bring iron, magnesium and other minerals, such as sulphur. These forces also have an iron-regulating effect. Many soils throughout the world contain large amounts of iron which cements the particles together to form what is known as an iron pan. The nettle preparation helps to break up these soils, releasing the iron.

Use the perennial *Urtica dioica*, not *Urtica urens* which is an annual with less sting. *U. dioica* is used in human internal medicine. A stinging nettle (*U. parviflora*) has been found in India which would probably make good 504; and it would be interesting to see whether the deadly New Zealand shrub ongaonga (*U. ferrox*) would work.

## Making the preparation

To make the preparation, harvest the nettles in late spring or early summer, before they flower. Dry the whole plant and keep them until you bury them in the ground in autumn. Stuff the dried plant into a round unglazed earthenware field tile, 10–15cm in diameter. Use a broom handle to firm the plant in the tile, and bury it in good soil in the autumn. Mark it well because the nettle preparation is buried for 12 months, until the following autumn. Alternatively you can dig a pit in which you make a kind of sandwich between sphagnum moss. Put a layer of moss down, then about 30–45cm of nettle well firmed down, with moss on the top. Cover with soil and mark well.

## Retrieving the preparation

When dug up, the nettle has shrunk away to just about 2.5cm of black 'compost' at the bottom of the tile. It is beautifully colloidal. I usually put the preparation through a sieve to break up the stalks before storing it.

The preparation is recovered by scraping off the moss first and then the decomposed nettle. Sieve and store. There should be no problem with it drying out during the settling-down stage.

## PREPARATION 505 OAK BARK — *Quercus robur*

Rudolf Steiner pointed out how important it was to have the right amount of calcium in the soil if the plants were to be healthy and free from disease. He said that the calcium brings harmony to the form of the plant and does not allow excesses of rampant growth to develop. This condition often arises when the moon forces are working too strongly during and after a wet period. For the calcium to have a healing effect, according to Steiner, it should be in a living form, and it is of no use if applied to the soil as a mineral.

The bark of the oak acts as an intermediary between the dead and the living. About 2.5–5 per cent of its substance is calcium. The oak bark is put into the skull of a domestic animal such as a cow, sheep or goat,

*Oak tree and leaf*

and buried in a watery environment such as a swamp, or in a water barrel surrounded by rotting plant material. Steiner does not say why the skull is used in this preparation, but a connection to the skull as a moon vessel can be seen if one studies embryology. In all embryo development, which Steiner points out is a moon-growth process, the skull appears first. Another example of the moon-growth process is seed germination, which is enhanced at the time of the full moon (for discussion of these processes, see Leivegoed 1951).

*Filling sheep's skull with oak bark 505*

As we are trying to regulate the calcium, we surround the bark in a bony 'container' which is built up from calcium. Placing the skull and the bark in a watery treatment will bring a balancing effect between the moon forces and the calcium.

The oak bark preparation will, over a period of time, raise the pH of the soil without the addition of lime. Agricultural lime applied to the land is made more effective where the oak bark preparation is used, and consequently less lime is required.

The European oak *Quercus robur* is used in temperate climates where it grows. *Q. alba* is used in the United States, and in India one of the evergreen oaks, *Q. dilatata* or *Q. glauca* is being used.

## Making the preparation

The preparation is made in autumn. The oak bark is grated to a fine powder with a rasp, then packed tightly into a domestic animal skull, preferably from a cow, bull or sheep.

All the flesh and brain material should be cleaned off the skull before it is used. In autumn, prepare a barrel of rainwater which is connected to a downpipe, so that the water is flowing in and out. Put plenty of rotting, smelly vegetation (leaves, grass etc) into the water in the barrel. Place the skull in the barrel amongst the rotting vegetation. You may need to put a heavy stone or brick on top of the skull to stop it floating to the surface.

Alternatively, choose a swampy area of land where there is a small flow of water and bury the skull in a hole at the edge of the swamp. Put rotting vegetable matter in the hole. It is a good idea to put the skull in a wirenetting cage and peg it down in case a flood washes it away.

### Retrieving the preparation

When you retrieve the skull in spring, split it to take out the preparation, which you put in a glass jar. It will still be smelly because it is anaerobic. Turn it every day until aerobic activity takes over and it smells quite sweet. This can take up to 14 days. Do not worry about white mycelium that grows on it during this time.

### PREPARATION 506 DANDELION — *Taraxacum officinale*

The dandelion flower belongs to the Compositae family. As a flower of Jupiter, it has a crystalline, silicic, cosmic form in a perfect sphere. Dandelion flowers that have gone to seed show the fluffy 'clock' form. The importance of silica is generally overlooked by conventional science, even though about 40 per cent of the earth's surface is of silica. Steiner points out how 'the silicic acid is needed to draw in the cosmic factor, and a thorough interaction must come about between the silicic acid in the plant and the potassium. We must look for a plant whose own potassium–silicic acid relationship will enable it to impart this power to the manure' (*Agriculture*, p103).

When making Preparation 506, the dandelion flowers are put in a cow mesentery. The mesentery is the 'skin' that holds all the digestive organs in the body of the cow. It is a very sensitive part of the body, and this sensitivity is imparted to the dandelion flowers during their period of preparation in the earth. Steiner notes that: 'This material can be added to the manure in the same way as before, and it will give the soil the ability to attract just as much silicic acid from the atmosphere and from the cosmos as is needed by the plants' (*Agriculture*, p103).

Preparation 506 gives the soil a living, ethereal quality with the ability to supply the substances that the plant needs.

### Making the preparation

Pick the dandelion flowers early in the morning before the sun is too high and the flowers have opened too fully. The flowers should be about half open, with the middle petals still folded inward like a kind of crown. If the flowers are too open when picked they will become very fluffy when dry; these should be discarded. Dry the flowers and store them in a similar manner as described for chamomile.

Cut off as much fat as possible from the mesentery (which can be obtained from an abattoir or from a home-kill butcher). Pile the flow-

*Dandelion*

ers onto it and fold the skin to make a tight 'parcel' which you tie up with string (see colour plate 5). Bury the parcel in the soil at a descending phase of the moon in autumn. Use the box system as described for the yarrow and mark well. You may need to protect it from being dug up by dogs.

## Retrieving the preparation
Dig up the preparation at the same time as you dig up the 500. You will find the mesentery is still intact and not broken down. Cut open the mesentery, remove the bulk of the preparation, scrape any broken-down flowers off the folds of the skin, and store in a glass jar. Preparation 506 should be regularly checked and gently aerated for the first few weeks after lifting to make sure it does not become anaerobic. Leave off the jar lid for the first few weeks.

*Making and using Preparations 502–508  81*

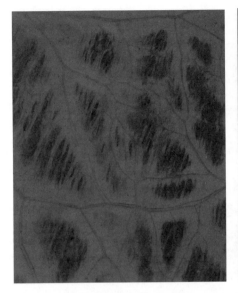

*Left: close-up of mesentery from a cow. Note that there is very little fat.*
*Right: dandelion Preparation 506 wrapped in mesentery parcel*

Steiner suggests, in *Agriculture*, that the Preparation 503 and 506 should spend six months hanging in a tree before being buried in the ground in a similar way to the stag's bladder. It is not yet known whether this treatment will make these preparations more effective.

## PREPARATION 507 VALERIAN — *Valeriana officinalis*

Valerian is a perennial plant which has a beautiful leaf with unusually patterned veins. Its triangular form makes it look almost detached from the earth. This form is an indication of its connection with the light forces. I once accidentally tipped over a bottle of the Valerian Preparation 507. When I later discovered it I found the contents had dried in the form of the valerian leaf. This shows how the plant products carry a memory of the plant form.

Valerian concentrates phosphorus, which is a vital constituent of plants, particularly the leaf, as it is involved in attracting the light used in photosynthesis. Preparation 507 stimulates the phosphate process and mobilises the phosphate-activating bacteria in the soil. Notice the connection between phosphorus, which burns with a white light, and the white valerian flowers. The flowers have a beautiful perfume. Valerian also brings the Saturn influence of warmth.

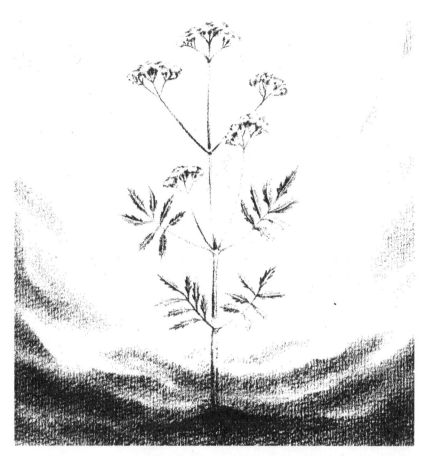

*Valerian*

*Valerian flowers ready for crushing in mortar and pestle*

*Making and using Preparations 502–508  83*

## Making the preparation

Valerian grows fairly easily from seed sown in spring or autumn in a seedbox protected from frost. It flowers early in the summer of the following year. Harvest the flowers in an ascending period when the moon is in an air/light constellation (Libra or Gemini). I have noticed that the keeping quality of the preparations is greatly enhanced if they are picked during this period. Grind the flowers with a pestle and mortar. Put them in a jar with four times their volume of distilled water — this makes a 20 per cent solution. Leave the jar on a windowsill for seven days then filter with a coffee filter. Put the preparation in a bottle, filled to overflowing, then cover to exclude air. Store in a dark cupboard.

## Using the preparation

To use Preparation 507, make up a 5 per cent solution, then stir one 10ml portion into 13.5 litres of rainwater for 10 minutes before applying. You will need 13.5 litres per acre. (Note that valerian is not put inside the compost heap like the other preparations but is spread over the top. Earthworms are very fond of it.)

The valerian preparation can also be spread over a crop to bring warmth. It raises the soil temperature by 1–2°C, so is very useful to protect sensitive plants from frost. This is particularly useful for avocado growers, who need a constant 14°C temperature for three days

*A selection of storage jars used for compost preparations; the jars are surrounded with peat and stored in a cool place*

for pollination. Make up a 5 per cent solution and stir as above, or put it through a flowform then spread it at the rate of 13 litres per acre. You can also spray this valerian solution on grain to improve germination.

## Storage
It is very important to store preparations well. They should be kept cool and moist (not wet) in glazed jars with loose-fitting lids in a peat-lined box or just surrounded by peat. *Never* put them in a refrigerator. They are best in a cool shady place, for example under a house or in a cellar.


## APPLICATION OF COMPOST PREPARATIONS TO THE COMPOST HEAP, LIQUID MANURE AND COWPAT PIT
Whenever you make a compost heap, liquid manure brew or a cowpat pit, finish it by putting the compost preparations in it. They will assist the breaking-down process and make the finished product more effective in the soil or on the plants. Each of the preparations acts like an organ in the human body. They work in balance with each other to organise the life processes.

You need one set of preparations — ie 1g each of Preparations 502–506 and 10ml of Preparation 507 — per 5 cubic metres (5 tonnes) of compost heap or per 200 litres of liquid manure. For a cowpat pit made with 60kg (one barrowload) of cow dung you need three sets of the preparations. These quantities are suitable for most conditions. In some European countries, twice this quantity of preparation is used.

*In the compost heap*
Wrap each solid preparation separately in material such as dried grass or old compost. Make fairly deep holes spaced out along one side of the compost heap and push each solid preparation into a separate hole and close the hole over well. Then make two holes in the top of the heap and pour one quarter of the stirred valerian in each hole and close the hole over. Sprinkle the rest of the liquid over and around the heap.

*In liquid manure*
Wrap each preparation separately in old compost or dried decayed grass and float on the top of the liquid manure. The 507 is sprinkled

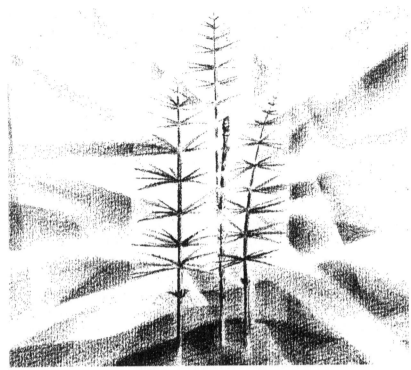

*Equisetum*

on the top after being stirred for 5–10 minutes.

*In the cowpat pit*
The preparations are simply pushed into the manure and the valerian is sprinkled over the top.

For small volumes of valerian, eg when using 200 litres of liquid manure or in the cowpat pit, rhythmically shake 10ml of 5 per cent solution in half a litre of water in a glass jar.

## PREPARATION 508 EQUISETUM — *Equisetum arvense*

This is one further preparation, which is not applied to the compost heap. Preparation 508 is made from the *Equisetum arvense* or horsetail plant, which grows in swampy wastes in Europe and Australia but is less common in New Zealand.

The equisetum plant has a very high silica content. If you burn it the carbon burns off, leaving a skeleton of silica. The preparation can therefore be used in a similar way to Preparation 501, to reduce excessive water forces around the plants and so reduce the risk of fungal disease. Equisetum does not bring the light forces that 501 does, so will not encourage plants to shoot to seed.

## Making the preparation
Harvest the plant in spring and dry it. Add it to rainwater at the rate of 100g per 2 litres of water. Bring it to the boil and let it simmer in a covered pan for 20 minutes, then leave it to stand for two days. Alternatively, you can soak the leaves in cold water for two weeks. The preparation should then have a good smell and is ready to use. Add 18 litres of water and stir as you would Preparation 500, for 10 minutes.

(Drs E and L Kolisko researched the effectiveness of different dilutions of equisetum. They found that the best results were obtained using a D5 solution. This is made by adding 10ml of the original solution to 90ml of distilled water, shaking it rhythmically for 2 minutes then adding 10ml of that solution to 90ml of distilled water and shaking and repeating this procedure a further 3 times.)

## Using the preparation
Spray the diluted preparation on the ground around the plants you want to protect just before stress times, for example just before full moon or perigee, when the moon is closest to the earth. Preparation 508 can be used frequently and it's a good idea to use it as part of your routine maintenance in early spring.

In Australia, Robert Williams suggested that *Casuarina stricta*, a sheoak which grows in the mountains, has been used as a substitute for equisetum with good results.

# EIGHT

# Conversion from a conventional to a biodynamic farm

## PASTORAL FARMS

To begin to be a successful biodynamic farmer you need first to have

good farming management skills. The decision to change from a conventional input–output system to using biodynamic techniques requires courage. You can no longer depend on 'quick fixes' to problems. But you can be reassured that many farmers have already taken this step and have built up successful biodynamic farms.

How does one go about converting a farm that has been managed conventionally to a biodynamic management system?

The same basic management changes will apply whether the farm is a dairy farm, a dry stock farm, an apple or kiwifruit orchard or a market garden. The conversion begins with the soil. You will need to start thinking about how a healthy soil life can be encouraged.

You will be extending your focus from quick growth over one or two years to sustaining the farm fertility for many years into the future. You'll stop working with the water-soluble fertilisers that damage soil structure and start building up the fertility and life of your soil. Stop using all chemical weed control! — these chemicals leave undesirable residues in the soil that inhibit the development of an active soil life.

First take stock of your farm and its condition. Look at what plants grow naturally on your farm, such as trees and weeds. They are a good indication of the soil characteristics. A proliferation of thistles and buttercups indicates a low soil pH.

The number of trees on your farm is also important. A farm needs adequate trees to provide shelter and shade for plants and animals. The trees benefit the environment, providing sustenance particularly for birds and bees. They also help to conserve moisture.

## The soil

What is the state of the soil on your farm? Is it open and aerated, containing earthworms and organic matter, or is it hard and compacted and 'dead'? What is the history of chemical inputs? The soil on most farms is likely to be pretty dead after many years of chemicals such as superphosphate, pugging by stock, and driving of heavy machinery over them. Have the soil tested for chemical residues such as DDT, cadmium and other heavy metals. You can't get Demeter certification for soil containing these substances; however, putting Preparation 500 on will accelerate their breakdown.

A soil test for available calcium and phosphorus is helpful, and soil bulk density is a good indication of its quality. Check the soil pH. A low pH, under about 5, reduces the availability of nutrients to plants and the preparations don't work so well.

If your soil test shows no measurable potash either in the topsoil or in the base rock, you will need to add potash — either the potash-rich rock feldspar or as sulphate of potash $K_2SO_4$. Never use the muriate (chloride of potash), as it contains damaging chlorine. Feldspar or the sulphate should be included in a compost heap or put into liquid manure to enliven it before applying to the land. Steiner recommended a liquid of the poisonous purple foxglove (*Agriculture*, p248).

Soils in estuarine areas and in some inland areas of Australia have a high salt content. On these soils you need to grow particular plants, such as mallee, which remove the salt. Such plants should always be grown between cropping areas.

The base rock the farm is on affects longterm mineral availability. The soil type and basic structure is also important. A sandy soil will always tend to dry out. You can turn most soils into good soil eventually, but it's better to start at least halfway there!

Don't despair if your soil is shallow and hard. One hill country farmer in the Waikato, New Zealand, started with hard, shallow soil, but after four years of applying biodynamic methods, plant roots on his farm can now penetrate more than a spade-depth down, and you can't even see the subsoil. His farm now looks greener than neighbouring farms, and there are no more slips, because water soaks into the soil instead of running off. The improved soil and pasture allow greater flexibility of grazing management than on surrounding farms.

## Water, climate, terrain and situation

Check the farm's drainage, and the availability of good quality water. The water should not have a high iron content.

The farm's terrain, aspect, and microclimate are all important. Which direction does the prevailing wind come from? In the southern hemisphere, a gently sloping northeast slope is ideal, particularly for fruit-growing. This aspect gives plentiful sun and less drying effect on the soil than a northwest slope. In the northern hemisphere the slope would need to face south or southeast. A slope is less subject to frost, which tends to collect in a valley.

Proximity to markets, transport and labour are important. What sheds and equipment do you already have? These will need to suit whatever farming projects you have in mind.

## Choice of farm enterprises

Your choice of farm enterprises should be based on all these characteristics of your farm that you have identified. Growing crops that are suitable for your particular farm is very important.

## Stock

Look at the type of stock carried on the farm. There are three great fertility tools farmers have at their disposal: the first is the cattle beast, the second, legumes (clover, lucerne, vetches) and the third, the farmer's greatest friend, the earthworm. In the case of a mixed farm, half the number of stock units carried on the farm should comprise cattle: their manure has a unique effect on soil fertility.

Begin to reduce the dependence that animals have on chemical drenches and dips by gradually replacing these with, for instance, cider vinegar and garlic drenches (see Appendix 4). It may take up to five years to eliminate the chemical drenches and dips completely in the case of sheep and goats. In the case of cattle, however, chemical drenches and dips can often be eliminated in a much shorter time. If it is necessary to use an allopathic drench, the animals should be put onto a quarantine paddock until the drench is eliminated. This will contain the contaminated dung, which will then not have a harmful effect on the rest of the farm.

On livestock farms stock-licks can provide trace element needs in the short term. It may also be possible to use various weeds to supply trace elements; for example, wing thistles made into a tea and used as a drench can supply needed copper (see Pfeiffer 1983, ch11).

Aim to establish a strong genetic base for your animals. Breed only from the healthy ones. Animal and plant health will improve as the soil becomes more alive from the use of the preparations.

## Improving the soil

European plants need a higher soil pH and more phosphorus than do New Zealand native grasses and trees.

*Lime*

Adding lime to the soil increases the numbers of worms and clover growth (see colour plate 3). You don't need a lot of lime because the Preparation 500 will enhance the calcium process. Lime stimulates soil processes and plant growth initially, but will also burn out the humus.

There are three forms of lime used in agriculture. The first is calcium carbonate, $CaCO_3$, which is known as agricultural lime or limestone rock, and is quarried. This form is ground fine and spread over paddocks. Burnt lime or rock lime, calcium oxide CaO, is made by burning $CaCO_3$ in a kiln. The third form is called hydrated or slaked lime. This is made by adding water to burnt lime. Hydrated lime, $Ca(OH)_2$, is a very fine powder and is the form recommended for use in compost-making. Note: for liming the soil, do not use dolomite $(Ca(Mg)CO_3)$ unless there is a known magnesium deficiency. Overuse of the mineral will increase the magnesium to a degree where it will upset the availability of potassium.

Aim to get the pH up to 5.8–6.5 for pasture of European grasses. An average loamy soil in New Zealand needs 500kg of agricultural lime $(CaCO_3)$ per acre, applied in the autumn. Then use Preparation 500 in the autumn and the spring. Lime may not be needed again for several years.

The rate of application of Preparation 500 varies between different countries. In New Zealand we have found 25g/acre to be effective. In Australia, 30g/acre is recommended, and in Germany, 100g/acre. For the first year you can get an additional effect from two applications, if possible in September and October (March and April in the northern hemisphere). This is more effective than increasing the quantity for one application. Aim to apply it around the time that dew starts to fall. After a while you will become sensitive to when is the best time to apply 500.

The compost preparations are also very important. You need one set for four acres each year. You will find that after several applications of these preparations your stock health improves dramatically. However, on sandy soil you don't get much effect until the soil has a good organic matter content.

The best way to apply the compost preparations over a large area is in liquid fertiliser. Use seaweed or thistles if these are plentiful, or cow manure. Put your seaweed or other material in a black polythene drum in a warm, sheltered place. Add the compost preparations as described in chapter 6.

You can apply the liquid fertiliser with the Preparation 500. Add the liquid fertiliser to the 500 for the last five minutes of stirring. The application rate is 13 litres of 500 and 2–3 litres of liquid fertiliser concentrate per acre.

Even better than liquid fertiliser is cowpat pit manure. The rate of use can vary (see chapter 6).

Preparation 501 should not be used during the first year, except maybe on a hay or silage paddock. Apply the 501 in the second year, after the first application of 500. Preparation 501 brings a quality to all plants which will improve the taste of the fruit or vegetables and the health of the animals. The timing of 501 application is important; for instance, it is best not to use it halfway through a grass growth period. Chapter 5 gives detailed instructions on when and how to apply 501.

*Phosphorus*
Phosphorus is also needed for plant growth, particularly leaf formation. The phosphorus is naturally cycled in New Zealand native bush and leaf mould, but is lost when the bush is removed. It does not occur naturally in most soils throughout the world and must therefore be added, to provide a healthy leaf-growth. Phosphorus, even when added in a soluble fertiliser, can also become insoluble in a dead soil, and so unavailable to plant life. You'll need to add phosphorus initially, as rock phosphate, which is acted on by soil organisms, making organic acids like in a compost heap. These organic acids can then be taken up by plants. Make sure the rock phosphate does not contain cadmium or other heavy metals, which is likely if it comes from Nauru or from North Carolina in the US.

In some areas of New Zealand which have been treated with a lot of contaminated phosphate, the sheep organs have a high cadmium content. Watch that you are not buying blood and bone fertiliser that comes from such animals. Reeds also take up cadmium, so cadmium can be removed from the soil by growing reeds, then burning them and recovering the cadmium from the ash.

'Sechura' phosphate from Egypt is a good uncontaminated source of phosphorus. It should be applied at the rate of 100kg per acre in spring when there is active grass growth.

*Potasssium*

If potassium is a component of the base rocks of much of your area (as it is in much of New Zealand), you do not have to add that mineral to the soil. Just grow deep-rooting plants and encourage earthworms, to bring the potassium up into the soil.

## New equipment needed

A new biodynamic practitioner will need an efficient mixing system — either machine or flowforms — with which to stir the biodynamic preparations, and some kind of sprayer to apply them. However, on smaller areas of up to 20 acres, you can stir and apply the preparations by hand. Details of stirring and applying the preparations and machinery and flowforms that can be used are given in Appendix 1. The pulsing of water in the flowforms seems particularly important and I advise putting your liquid fertiliser through the flowforms also (see chapter 4).

## Planetary influences

As you become more confident in your approach to biodynamic management, you will find it useful to acquire a working knowledge of the way the moon and other planetary rhythms affect the whole management system. Some information on planetary rhythms is given in the next chapter; and see Maria Thun (1979) and, in New Zealand, the BioDynamic Association's *BioDynamic Farming and Gardening Calendar.*

## DAIRY FARMS

Much of what has been said in this chapter applies also to dairy farms. Most dairy farms will be pretty dead, after years of application of superphosphate and urea. But the farm may have good potential, particularly if it is on pumice, where the soil can be deep and well drained.

*Shorthorn beef cattle on a biodynamic farm*

Many paddocks on dairy farms in wet areas have suffered from pugging over the years. You need to prevent further pugging by having somewhere to overwinter cattle, where they won't do so much damage to the soil structure. It is not good for the animals to stand on wet ground — they need a dry pad or a barn. It is important not to stress your animals. The stocking rate should not be too high — no more than one cow per acre in New Zealand — and you should always have feed ahead of your cows.

You may have some animal health problems during the farm conversion stage. If you use allopathic medicine on a cow, eg drench for bloat, you have to quarantine the cow. After one treatment of penicillin the cow cannot be certified as Demeter for two years. There are homeopathic remedies available. For mastitis you can use garlic, aloe vera, marjoram or lemon balm in cider vinegar. A garlic and nasturtium and cider vinegar drench is effective against bloat; and it does not taint the milk if given just after milking. Cider vinegar is a good tonic — put two litres in the drinking trough each day, or sprinkle it on the hay (see Appendix 4).

Some cows will adapt to the new regime more easily than others. Naturally you would have to give allopathic medicine rather than see an animal suffer, but do not breed from cows that need such medicine, and gradually cull them. I once had a cow that kept getting mastitis in the front right quarter, and its calf also got mastitis in the same quarter. I finally had to cull the cow and calf.

The health of the animals may take two years to improve, but sometimes bloating stops as soon as you start to use 500 on the pastures.

Calves need good management. Suckle them on nurse cows, three per cow. Wean no earlier than three months old; four months is better.

Gradually change the pasture sward to include a wider variety of plant species, for instance deep-rooting plants such as chicory, red clover, lucerne and cocksfoot which improve the soil structure. This variety of species will bring health to the livestock by means of diversity of diet, and will also bring more minerals into the farm system. A suggested herbal ley mixture is given in Appendix 5. You can increase the number of grass species on your farm by making hay from a herbal ley and feeding the hay all round the farm.

Make sure you have sufficient hay and/or silage. Aim for two years' supply, because the weather can be uncertain. Establish a rhythm on the farm, for example with preparation- and fodder-making, to make up for vagaries in the weather. Cut the hay and silage when the moon is ascending and in Gemini if possible. Even if it rains it won't spoil, particularly if you applied Preparation 501 during a period when the moon and Saturn were in opposition one week before.

Grow crops for feeding in a dry summer or for making silage. Maize is best, chopped up. A good winter crop is Italian ryegrass and red clover or oats.

## Cowshed effluent

The dung droppings and the urine of cows during the time they are in the milking shed or parlour is a very valuable source of fertility. In New Zealand it is often discarded by farmers, who see it as something to be 'got rid of'; usually it is hosed down a drain into a pond. Here it is supposed to go through an oxidation process before it may or may not be spread over the farm.

Some farmers have a large 'sacrifice' paddock near the cowshed onto which the effluent is pumped each day. This results in a wet soggy paddock and a build-up of nitrogen with resultant unpalatable grass.

The biodynamic farmer will run the effluent over a Virbela flowform for an hour and will add some cowpat pit to introduce the preparations before spreading onto the land. This will stabilise nitrogen in the liquid.

Another option is to put cowpat pit liquid manure through the flowform for about 20 minutes and introduce this into the effluent pond. This will quickly break down the solid material and can be spread over the farm after a week.

*Cowshed effluent being flowed through a Virbela VB500; sucked into a tanker;*

In both cases the effluent can then be pumped over the farm through a travelling irrigator, or spread with a liquid-manure wagon. In this way the whole farm can be treated. It will take about two years to get over the whole farm. Farmers have reported that cows will go on eating grass immediately after the spreading of the treated effluent. They also report an increase in clover growth; and there have been reports of a decrease in incidents of mastitis.

Some biodynamic farmers collect the solid manure for compost-making, which means there is less effluent to deal with. Farmers in India also collect cow urine for making compost and liquid manure.

## SHEEP, BEEF AND CROPPING FARMS

Ideally a farm should have at least 30 per cent of flat land and you should be able to drive a tractor over most of the farm. A dry shingle area is good for wintering cattle and strong clay/silt country is suitable for withstanding summer drought and for cropping. The best location is within 30–40km of saleyards. Check water availability, trees, nutrient status of the soil, fences, gates, woolshed and cattle yards. Do a budget, including all the inputs needed.

The pasture will need less lime and phosphate than a dairy farm. You could apply these and the biodynamic preparations on a section each year as your budget allows. More intensive applications would

*. . . and sprayed onto pasture. Preparations 502–507
and cowpat pit have been added*

be needed on cropping areas. On large, hilly areas you may have to apply the preparations from the air. You then apply liquid manure with the Preparation 500.

The cropping area must be fertile. To grow one ton of wheat you need 40kg nitrogen. One cattle beast gives 20kg nitrogen per year, so you would need the build-up from several years' grazing before you can grow a crop. Including legumes in the pasture helps to build up nitrogen, and applying the preparations encourages worm activity and build-up of humus. Weeds are a good indicator of how fertile the paddock is: if there are lots of flat weeds such as broad-leaved plantain, it is not fertile enough for cropping.

When you buy in stock you must first keep them in a quarantine paddock. Find out what they've been drenched with. Avoid buying stock that have had Ivomectin. (Ivomectin is a synthetic material that is such an efficient internal worm drench that it kills earthworms as well. Its effects last in the dung a number of years, so dung from animals treated with this material will not break down.) Animals take on the certification of the farm after they've been there for two years. Those conceived and born on a Demeter farm can be certified as full Demeter.

Suitable stocking rates will generally be between three to five stock units per acre, depending on the area. Aim to have even numbers of stock units in cattle and sheep. (One adult cattle beast is one stock unit, equivalent to five adult sheep.)

Your aim will be to get the nutrients cycling so that you don't need to add minerals or trace elements; in fact adding trace elements could upset the balance. Regular application of the biodynamic preparations will ensure that the soil is working biodynamically and ordering the cycling processes. Of course some nutrients are lost when products are sold off the farm, but this is mainly carbon. Most minerals are recycled, and are also synthesised by the plants. Most of the calcium in milk does not come from the land, but is synthesised in the cow.

If the grass is eaten down low at the start of spring, it will take some time to get going. Growing a feed crop to use when grass is in short supply will help prevent overgrazing. But don't let animals onto a crop during wet weather. It's better to turn the crop into silage and feed it out.

After applying biodynamic practices for a few years you'll find your farm will develop into a self-contained entity. The healthiness of the soil, pasture and animals will be evident.

# NINE

# Conversion from a conventional to a biodynamic farm — orchards and vineyards

 You may be considering converting an established orchard to biodynamic management or planting a new orchard on bare land. If you have a choice, the latter is easier, as you won't know what has been put on the soil of an established orchard.

If you are converting an established orchard, find out whether the varieties of trees that have been planted are suitable for that environment. Some varieties are better suited to biodynamic methods than others; for instance, Gala will always be susceptible to blackspot.

How are the trees grown — espalier or with single leaders? What shelterbelts are there?

Try to find out what chemicals have been used in the past. How compact is the soil? If there is a lot of moss in the spray strip, the soil is therefore badly compacted and will take at least three years to get it right. You will also need to consider what spraying is being done on neighbouring orchards and how close they are.

Be aware of the frost liability, particularly if you are growing stonefruit. It is better to plant on a slope where the air drains down than at the bottom of the slope.

## CONVERTING AN EXISTING PIPFRUIT OR STONEFRUIT ORCHARD

The first job is to establish a good herbal ley between the trees (see Appendix 5). You may have to disc up the soil and put in a green crop first. Repeat this for a second year, to get the soil active, before putting in the ley.

The aim is not to have to irrigate the trees, as this prevents the roots from growing properly. Encourage the roots to go deeper with plenty of humus.

Start making compost at the beginning. You'll need at least 10 tonnes per acre. You'll also need cows on the property. For each five acres of orchard, set aside one acre to run one cow. Cows can be put in a yard at night and the dung collected daily to be used in the compost or for liquid manure. Cows are more useful than poultry: note that raw manure from poultry if uncomposted can taint the fruit. Besides, to keep enough poultry to provide sufficient manure for the trees would make a lot of mess. If you do decide to keep poultry, geese would be more effective than chickens, as geese eat insects.

## ESTABLISHING A NEW PIPFRUIT OR STONEFRUIT ORCHARD

Look for a property large enough to include an area to run cattle — not so much for milk production as to provide dung for making compost. If there is also room for growing vegetables you will be able to grow plenty of material for making compost.

Select trees that have a proven record of being disease-resistant in that district. Now that there is a growing demand from Europe for products grown in an environmentally friendly way, researchers in New Zealand have been developing varieties that are resistant to diseases such as blackspot and mildew. There are now about seven promising varieties as a result of crossing varieties such as Braeburn, Gala and Cox's Orange with other Malus species such as crabapple, *Malus floribunda*.

*A biodynamic tree and shrub nursery*

A few New Zealand nurseries, such as Tree Dimension Nursery in Motueka, have old varieties of apple trees. Many of these, such as the russet apples, do not have much consumer appeal but still taste fine.

## Shelter

The purpose of shelter is to break up the blasts of wind which will stop the trees growing. Shelter should filter the air rather than stop it with a solid wall of trees. It should not be too dense, and good air movement should be possible at all times. The side facing the sun should be deciduous; the side facing the cold winter winds, where protection is needed, can be more dense, with a mixture of deciduous and evergreen trees. Avoid planting any species with vigorous roots, for example willow. For a list of some species suitable for New Zealand conditions, see 'Shelter' in chapter 10. All species should be trimmable.

## Planting

Plant new trees into cultivated soil, 3-4 metres apart. If they are too close there will be insufficient airflow, which increases the risk of disease. When planting, fill the holes with a mixture of soil and compost, and also spread compost around the trees on the soil surface. The compost should have been made with the compost preparations, as described in chapter 6.

Keep grass and weeds away from the young trees by mulching with hay or straw, as grass roots seem to inhibit the roots of young

*Shelterbelt consisting of mixed varieties of trees*

*Conversion from conventional to biodynamic orchards 101*

fruit trees. The mulch should be spread to at least one metre out from the trees, but should not touch the tree stems.

You can grow potatoes between the rows in the first year as a catch crop. Then, in autumn, sow a herbal ley containing chicory, red clover, lucerne and cocksfoot. This can be cut for the first time in spring. The ley will eventually provide a great mulch.

Don't install a drip-type irrigation system, or the tree roots will not grow down deep into the soil. You should not need to water the trees at all, even in very dry areas, if you have, with good biodynamic management, established a structured soil with a high humus content.

## APPLICATION OF THE BIODYNAMIC PREPARATIONS ON NEW AND ESTABLISHED ORCHARDS

Spray with Preparation 500 twice in the autumn and twice in the spring in the first year. In the second year, three sprays of 500 should be sufficient. Fruitgrowers in New Zealand may have to keep applying 500 at that rate permanently to combat the effects of the hole in the ozone layer: in some areas, avocados are getting sunburned two months before they are ready for picking.

Equisetum or Preparation 501, applied at the apogee and when the moon and Saturn are in opposition, help to suppress fungal growth. If they are also sprayed after harvest, they enhance the strength of the next year's fruiting buds.

Spray with cowpat pit liquid or with liquid compost at a time approaching full moon during the growing season. Seaweed liquid manure is also useful (see chapter 6).

### Tree paste
The three ingredients of tree paste — clay, sand and cow manure — represent the three basic components of soil, which are united by the Preparation 500. Steiner spoke of the tree as being like soil raised up above the earth's surface; the bark is like the surface of the soil, and the twigs that grow each year are like annual plants growing out of the earth. Steiner also compared the cambium — the growing layer under the bark — to the roots which support these 'annual plants'. The tree paste nourishes and strengthens the 'bark/soil' and the cambium of the tree, to make it healthy.

Apply tree paste in the winter — after pruning but before budburst, and at a descending moon time — to stimulate tree growth.

*Tree paste*

1 part cow manure

1 part silica sand or diatomaceous earth

1 part potting clay or bentonite

Mix these together with stirred Preparation 500 — sufficient to make a thin paste. For a small number of trees the paste can be painted on with a whitewash brush, as high as you can reach.

For a commercial orchard, the paste should be thin enough to be sprayed. Make it with bentonite and diatomaceous earth, rather than potting clay and silica sand, so it easier to spray. Make sure the paste has been strained to remove any objects that could block the pump or nozzle. Also, choose a coarse nozzle and use a centrifugal rather than a diaphragm pump;. the latter would be damaged by the nature of the materials.

The paste can be applied to all fruit trees and vines, but it should not be sprayed onto citrus trees, just applied around the base.

## DISEASE CONTROL

If disease-resistant varieties have been planted it should be possible to avoid spraying fungicidal compounds on the trees. Other varieties can have one or two sprays of weak copper per year if necessary, when the trees are older. On already established orchards you will have to spray against pests and disease at first. Copper sulphate, copper oxychloride or similar compounds are suitable fungicides. In New Zealand the Demeter standards allow 1.2kg/acre per year of copper spray — this could be applied in three sprays of 400g/acre. The first spray should be before bud-burst. Spray copper or sulphur early before petal-fall against blackspot in apples and leafcurl in peaches. Later in the season spray 501 or equisetum just before a full moon, particularly at apogee, to protect trees against fungus disease.

Application of liquid fertiliser such as seaweed or nettles strengthens the plants. However, you can't beat the black spot on conventional apple varieties, unless it is a very dry spring. Feed the plants well-balanced compost. High concentrations of nitrogen cause 'blow-out' of fruit, making them more susceptible to fungus and pests.

Pheromone twist-ties can be used against codling moth. Building up a predator population on companion host plants also helps.

*Conversion from conventional to biodynamic orchards 103*

## SUBTROPICAL FRUIT TREES
Citrus, kiwifruit, avocados, persimmon, passionfruit, tamarillos and feijoas all need similar treatment.

### Citrus
A citrus orchard is easy to convert to biodynamic management. Citrus trees are surface rooters and they like plenty of compost around their roots. Also apply compost over the whole area at the rate of 4–10 tonnes/acre. Compost for citrus should contain at least 10 per cent cow manure, as this will supply many of the trace elements needed for good citrus growth. Apply liquid fertiliser, especially seaweed, nettle and liquid cowpat pit, each month. Apply Preparation 500 three times a year. Preparation 501 is good for improving the taste of citrus. Apply it after flowering, when the fruit is just set, at a time when the moon and Saturn are in opposition.

*Disease control*
The main disease problems of citrus are from melanose fungus which causes spotted fruit, and verrucosis fungus (*Elsinoe fawcetti*) which causes corky growth on fruit and leaves, particularly in areas with high humidity, such as Northland, Bay of Plenty and South Auckland in New Zealand. A spray of weak copper at petal fall should control these diseases. Also, collect and burn all diseased fruit.

Uncomposted animal manures, particularly chicken manure which has a high ammonia content, can cause very soft growth which encourages scale and aphids. The aphids exude honeydew on which black mildew grows, so that the fruit needs washing. So always use well matured compost!

You need constant vigilance against borer, which can only be controlled manually. When harvesting, cut out any affected branch and burn it. You can kill borer by poking a piano wire down the borer hole.

### Avocado
Avocados need a well-drained soil, as they are susceptible to Phytophthera (an indigenous soil fungus which attacks the roots of many exotic trees) when they get to about 11–12 years old. They also need plenty of compost to maintain a high fertility to support the surface feeding roots. Avocado leaf mould contains a certain amount of phosphate, so encourage the build-up of leaf mould around the trees.

*Hass avocados growing in a biodynamic orchard*

Avocados may be infested by leafroller, but this is not generally a problem. Leafroller can be controlled by spraying with *Bacillus thuringensis* (BT).

## Persimmon

Persimmon also need plenty of compost. They tend to get mealybugs under the calyx. These can be reduced by pyrethrum or garlic sprays. Chilli pepper, garlic and ginger is an effective spray used in India against various pests.

## Feijoa

Feijoas are easy to grow and do well in northern and eastern coastal areas of New Zealand. The fruit are difficult to market as they are watery, and have a short shelf-life. Feijoa trees tend to suffer from scale if too sheltered. The branches need to be thinned regularly and the last season's growth pruned. Give a small amount of compost and spray with Preparations 500 and 501.

## Passionfruit

Passionfruit are normally grown from seed, and the plant usually lasts about three years. They need plenty of biodynamic compost, water and spraying with Preparation 500. Spraying 501 at the time when the moon is in opposition to Saturn will control most of the fungus.

### Tamarillo

Tamarillos are quick-growing. They are much sweeter when grown biodynamically than conventionally; nitrogenous fertiliser makes them bitter. They are gross feeders, so use plenty of biodynamic compost — at least 10 tonnes per acre. Prune the plants after fruiting. Foliar feed once a month with biodynamic seaweed liquid manure.

Mildew on the leaves can be controlled by applying Preparation 501 at a time when the moon and Saturn are in opposition.

### Preparation 501

Spray all subtropical fruit with Preparation 501 when the fruit is set, at a time when the moon and Saturn are in opposition, to improve fruit quality. Regular sprayings of 501 at this time will also strengthen the plants against mildew.

## VINEYARDS

For a new vineyard, you may need to rip the soil before planting. Dip the vine roots in a mixture of Preparation 500 and cow manure before planting them. Alternatively you can spray on the 500 after planting, then again twice in spring and once in autumn. Grow three successive green crops between the rows after planting: first plant oats and vetch in early spring — disc into the soil in late summer; then tick beans and lupins in autumn — disc into the soil in late spring; and then barley and red clover — disc into the soil in late summer. After the third green crop you can put down a herbal ley, which should include cocksfoot, dandelions, chicory, plantain, mustard and Montgomery red clover.

Mulch the vines with hay or straw, but watch that it is not contaminated with chemical residues. Put on liquid fertiliser — fish or seaweed, bonemeal or blood and bone, and plenty of compost. You should also apply a dressing of reactive rock phosphate before sowing the second green crop. Planting some manuka trees nearby will protect the vines from mealy bug.

*TEN*

# Commercial and home vegetable production

 The successful production of a wide range of high-quality organically grown vegetables is probably the most satisfying achievement of any of the horticultural disciplines. It is also the most necessary and important, as vegetables play a large part in most people's diet. For this reason it is almost obligatory that vegetables for human consumption be grown to the highest quality without the use of chemical fertilisers or the possibility of residual pesticides.

Organic vegetable production is the most demanding of all crops, in terms of expertise and management skills, particularly to maintain a continuity of crop. It is hoped that the following guidelines will encourage more people to grow vegetables biodynamically.

## SITE SELECTION

When starting out to grow vegetables, you can give yourself a great advantage if you choose a good block of land to suit the crops you will grow. Six things to consider are: aspect, soil type, climate, shelter, water supply and proximity to market.

### Aspect

Choose land facing the morning sun: northeast in the southern hemisphere, and southeast in the northern hemisphere. This aspect will warm up more quickly in the spring, and will have less tendency to dry out than land which is subjected to the baking effect of the afternoon sun.

The land should be as level as possible: a slight slope to the northeast (to the southeast in the northern hemisphere) is an advantage for some crops, but make sure you can use machinery easily. I have however seen a very successful market garden on quite a steep sunny hillside that had been terraced.

*A farm that has been managed biodynamically for 25 years*

Make sure the land you buy is not wet and swampy or likely to flood.

### Soil type
Look for fertile soil — it helps. A silty loam is the ideal. But check the soil's behaviour in climatic extremes; for example:
- How quickly does it dry out?
- What is it like when it becomes wet?
- Is it easy to cultivate?
- How deep is the topsoil?
- What is the drainage like?
- What is the underlying rock and is there a hard pan?
- What is the land's growing history?
    Of course the physical nature of the soil will be improved with the increase of the humus content through biodynamic management.

### Climate
Climate is important in determining what crops can be grown and when. Aspects to look at are:
- The distribution of rainfall
- Is the land frost-free, or how severe are the frosts?
- How soon does the land warm up in spring?
- How does the autumn temperature affect growth?
Local climatic conditions are possibly more important to consider:
- Is the land in a frost pocket?
- Is it exposed to the prevailing wind?

- Is it in rain shadow (in an area that gets less rain than the normal district rainfall)?

Some areas and climates are especially suited to particular crops, for example in New Zealand brussels sprouts grow well in South Canterbury, swedes in Southland and tomatoes and sweetcorn in Hawke's Bay.

## Shelter

Good shelter can be a decided advantage for maximising the performance of the market garden land. Shelter from the chilling effects of the southerly or the drying effects of a nor'wester can be provided by well-planted tree shelter. Much has been written on the subject of shelter; there is an excellent chapter on the subject in John and Bunny Mortimer, *Trees for the New Zealand Countryside* (1984). This chapter will point the market gardener to the many species available and the position to plant.

The lie of the land is also an important consideration. For instance, it is an advantage if the land slopes away from the prevailing cold or drying winds.

As shelterbelt planting I would recommend for New Zealand, alder *Alnus rubra* or *A. glutinosa* or *Casuarina cunninghamiana*, and *Casuarina glauca* for near the sea; and for low trimmable shelter, the New Zealand native plants — pittosporum (*Pittosporum eugenioides, tenuifolium* and *crassifolium*), kowhai (*Sophora microphylla*) or akeake (*Dodonea viscosa*), totara (*Podocarpus totara*) and taupata (*Coprosma repens*), to name a few suitable for salt winds. The Australian *Banksia integrafolia* is a wonderfully versatile tree. It grows from the coast to the centre of both islands in New Zealand. In other countries advice on suitable species should be sought from arborists.

## Water supply

Check water supply, availability and quantity and quality. Look particularly at the iron content in the water — iron is not conducive to making good liquid manures.

## Proximity to markets

Travelling, transport and freight are very expensive in both time and resources. Positioning your farm close to the market means you, the grower, can have a good relationship with the consumer. This can

*Commercial and home vegetable production 109*

also provide an important social aspect: customers can visit your farm and see how their vegetables are grown.

## SOIL FERTILITY MANAGEMENT

The maintenance and improvement of soil fertility in a market garden must be well thought through. A good management plan will ensure that the soil fertility will improve year by year.

The main consideration is the building up of the permanent humus in the soil. This can be done by:

• growing green manure (eg vetch and oats) between production crops
• using adequate amounts of compost
• adding liquid manures and the cowpat pit
• regular application of Preparation 500.

### Crop rotation

A tool to maintain soil structure and humus is a well-planned crop rotation. It is a good idea to have sufficient land to return preferably half the land to growing soil-sustaining crops — either green crops or permanent pasture (for an example of a rotation, see Table 10.1). Putting land back into permanent pasture is the quickest way to increase its humus content. Also, with intelligent use of all the preparations, it is possible to maintain a fertile, healthy soil forever.

### Green manuring

The wonderful thing about legumes in a strongly active biodynamic soil is that they can accumulate nitrogen out of the atmosphere at no cost. There are two main times for sowing green crops: autumn and spring.

Always sow a grain together with a legume, for example in autumn use rye grain or oats (black or white) together with either blue lupin, tick beans or hairy vetch.

Best results are obtained if you sow in early autumn, at a time when the moon and Saturn are in opposition. This crop would be turned into the soil just before the plant flowers.

If you sow in spring, use wheat, barley or oats together with blue lupins, broad beans, tick beans or vetch. Other species suitable for green manuring are mustard or phacelia (blue bee flower). Again, best results are obtained if you sow these in the period just before the moon and Saturn are in opposition in spring. Many combinations of

TABLE 10.1: Suggested crop rotation for a market garden

| Year | | Plot 1 | Plot 2 | Plot 3 | Plot 4 |
|---|---|---|---|---|---|
| 1 | Autumn | WVC[1] | WGC[2] | PP[3] | PP |
|   | Spring | SGC[4] | SVC[5] | PP | PP |
| 2 | Autumn | WVC | WGC | PP | PP |
|   | Spring | SGC | SVC | PP | PP |
| 3 | Autumn | Sow PP | WGC | WVC | PP |
|   | Spring | PP | Sow PP | SGC | SVC |
| 4 | Autumn | PP | PP | WVC | WGC |
|   | Spring | PP | PP | SGC | SVC |
| 5 | Autumn | WVC | PP | Sow PP | WGC |
|   | Spring | SGC | SVC | PP | Sow PP |
| 6 | Autumn | WVC | WGC | PP | PP |

1 WVC = Winter vegetable compost
2 WGC = Winter green crop — ryecorn or oats (black and white) together with blue lupin or tick beans or vetch.
3 PP = Permanent pasture — Italian rye, cocksfoot, red clover, white clover.
4 SGC = Summer green crop — oats, barley, wheat together with blue lupin or broad beans or tick beans, phacelia or mustard.
5 SVC = Summer vegetable compost

species are possible, to give a wide variety that can be grown each season. This will allow a crop rotation within the green manuring programme.

A spring-sown crop would be ready to turn in about mid summer, before flowering and before the formation of seed. This is because at the time of seed formation the proteins in the leaf are being translocated to the seed; thus there would be less protein content in the crop to be converted into available nitrogen to feed the following production crop. On the other hand if the green crop is left longer to mature, the higher carbonaceous material will add structure to the soil when turned in.

*Commercial and home vegetable production 111*

In turning the green crop in, it is best to use disc harrows to chop up the crop and incorporate it into the soil. The seedbed should be made with spring tyne cultivators. A rotary hoe is not a good tool to use because, although it turns in the green leafy crop satisfactorily, it can pulverise the soil and thus destroy the structure of the soil. It can also kill earthworms.

## Compost application
The making of compost is described in chapter 6.

Compost can be used in various stages of decomposition. When it is not fully broken down it will be higher in nitrogen and suitable for leafy crops. When well broken down it will be higher in carbon and more suitable for substance crops such as potatoes, kumara (sweet potato), sweetcorn, beans, squash etc. Remember that overuse of nitrogenous compost can cause plants to grow too rampantly and thus become susceptible to fungus and insect attack.

To feed the crop in a market garden, compost should be used at the rate of 20 cubic metres per acre.

Compost can be used in many ways. It can be broadcast in the spring over an area before growing a heavy-feeding field crop of potatoes, pumpkins or squash. It can be placed in furrows under crops such as brassicas, lettuce, tomatoes and various cucurbits for spring and autumn planting. Alternatively it can be broadcast in autumn over the area that is going to be sown in green crop, which will encourage green manure growth and give a consequent increase in fertility derived from the turning in and breakdown of the crop. An area so treated would be suitable for salads and brassicas.

## Application of liquid manures
Liquid manure is an effective plant tonic, particularly when it has been made using biodynamic Preparations 502–507. Liquids made from cow manure and cow urine, stinging nettle, seaweed and various weeds can be used at fortnightly intervals at the rate of 1:10, for example 4.5 litres of liquid manure to 45 litres of water per acre. (See chapter 6 for instructions on preparing/making liquid manure.)

Spray the liquid towards evening when the dew is beginning to fall, just before full moon or around when the moon is in opposition to Saturn. It is a good idea to stir or put the mixture through a flow-form for 10 minutes before applying.

## How to use the cowpat pit

The cowpat pit has proved very effective when used as a liquid manure to bring health and vitality to the crops. It is a valuable way of bringing the influence of the Preparations 502–507 into the market garden.

Instructions on how to prepare a cowpat pit are given in chapter 6. Use at the rate of 1kg in 45 litres of water per acre.

## Application of Preparation 500

Apply Preparation 500 at least twice a year, in spring and autumn, in a descending period of the moon (in New Zealand, see the BioDynamic Association's *BioDynamic Farming and Gardening Calendar*). Apply in the afternoon at the rate of 25g (one portion) per acre (see chapter 4 and Appendix 1).

It has been found over the years that this preparation improves soil quality in terms of structure, water-holding capacity and humus formation, encourages a deeper root penetration and strong, upright growth in plants, and brings an increase in earthworm activity.

## Application of Preparation 501 (horn silica)

Usually Preparation 501 is applied when Preparation 500 is seen to be working, 12 months after first application. It is applied in spring and summer on an ascending period of the moon (see the *BioDynamic Farming and Gardening Calendar*). Apply early in the morning, just after sunrise, at the rate of 1g of 501 in 13 litres of warmed rainwater per acre (see chapter 5).

Timing of application is important. The general rule is to apply Preparation 501 at an early stage in plant development, eg at the four-leaf stage, and again just before harvest. The effect of this is to enhance the photosynthesis process; and it also seems to improve product quality, taste and shelf-life.

I have found over the years that spraying in the morning, just before the moon and Saturn are in opposition, will strengthen the plant against fungus and often against insect attack also (see chapter 11 on calcium and silica).

## Preparations 502–507

These are incorporated into the composts, liquid manures and cowpat pit and applied.

Over the years I have found that the use of these preparations improves the fermentation processes in the breakdown of all bio-mass. The effect, as the preparations work through the composts, liq-uid manures and cowpat pit, is to improve the vegetables noticeably in terms of growth, quality, taste, freedom from pests and disease and shelf-life.

## TIMING OF OPERATIONS

Market gardeners using biodynamic management will endeavour to become conversant with the rhythms of the moon. There are six rhythms that it is useful to know about:

1 the waxing and waning of the moon (new moon and full moon)
2 the time when the moon and Saturn are in opposition
3 ascending and descending
4 the perigee and apogee (the time when the moon is closest to and furthest from the earth respectively)
5 the node (the time when the moon's path and the sun's path coin-cide)
6 the rhythm of the moon's path through the constellations.

All the rhythms except that of the moon and Saturn in opposition are discussed in Maria Thun 1979 (extracts are included in the BioDynamic Association's *BioDynamic Farming and Gardening Calendar*). The opposition between the moon and Saturn is discussed in chapter 11.

Using the available knowledge of these moon rhythms it is possi-ble for the market gardener to choose an appropriate cosmic time to carry out any market-gardening operation.

### Seed sowing

I have found, with 30 years' experience, that there is always a good germination at the time of full moon and also at the time of moon/Saturn opposition. However, plants germinated at the full moon are likely to be soft and leggy, whereas those germinated when the moon and Saturn are in opposition have more strength and struc-ture, and are likely to develop into strong plants that can resist dis-ease and pests.

Sowing seeds or cultivating the soil at appropriate times accord-ing to the moon in a particular constellation can enhance the inherent nature of the plant in question. For example, sowing or cultivating carrots when the moon is in Virgo, which is an earth constellation, definitely produces superior carrots; and sowing or cultivating lettuces when the moon is in a water constellation, eg Cancer or Scorpio, produces very good lettuces (see Thun 1979, p19).

## Seed varieties

Use open pollinated seeds rather than hybrids, if you can obtain them; and choose known quality cultivars suitable for your district.

Avoid genetically engineered plants. The introduction of a gene into a plant to give it resistance to a certain insect or to a weedicide, for instance, is Bandaid therapy. Dealing with insects or weeds in this way doesn't solve the root of the problem. Besides, what can be done when the insects become immune to that particular introduced insecticide gene? And what will that gene do to the person eating the food? Might it lead to future unexplained illnesses?

## Transplanting seedlings

Transplant seedling vegetables when the moon is in a descending period. This particular 14-day period encourages very quick root development, since the growth energies are directed more towards the soil. This is probably one of the most useful rhythms for the market gardener when transplanting seedlings; provided plants receive adequate water, planting losses are dramatically reduced.

The occurrence of the node, which is approximately every 13.7 days, should always be noted as a time when no gardening operations should be carried out. The time from at least six hours before the node to three hours after should be avoided.

## Disease and pest control

Remember that when the moon is approaching full or when it is close to the earth (the perigee) is a time when there is much moisture in the earth. This is when fungus can proliferate, so precautions should be taken — for example, using silica preparations such as 501 or 508 equisetum — to help to counteract the excess moisture.

Pests will also become rampant at full moon, so be aware of insect attacks, and take precautions.

## CULTIVATION AND WEED CONTROL

### Cultivation

Generally one wants to be as gentle as possible in the cultivation of the soil. Heavy tractors, deep ploughing and rotary hoeing are to be avoided.

*Commercial and home vegetable production 115*

When breaking in new land, disc up the pasture twice in autumn, allowing time for the turf to die off. Lightly plough to no deeper than 10cm, using a disc and harrow. If you avoid deep ploughing you will still be working within the living topsoil layer. Subsequent working-up of paddocks after a crop has been harvested can be done by chopping up the crop remains with discs, and making a seed or planting bed with the crumbler tiller. Any compost is spread before the discing. This is still working within the top 10cm of soil.

## Incorporating a green crop
Run the disc over the green crop until it is worked into the soil. Leave it for three weeks, then work up the seedbed with a crumbler tiller.

## Irrigation
You should not generally need to irrigate plants growing in soil that has been biodynamically managed and so has a reasonable humus content and good structure, as their roots penetrate deep into the soil. Remember that irrigating during a hot period will intensify the breakdown of the all-important humus, and will also bring the roots to the surface of the soil. Consequently the plants will then need more irrigation.

Much of the irrigation water used in the heat of the day will evaporate and be lost to the immediate water circulatory system. A general improvement of soil structure throughout the vegetable-growing areas of the world, by using biodynamic methods, would save the world millions of litres of water annually. This is particularly important where groundwater supplies are diminishing.

## Weeding
Remember, one year's seeding means seven years' weeding. If planting and sowing are done accurately, with the right spaces between rows, it is possible to set up a system whereby cultivators mounted on a tractor toolbar can effectively deal with weeds.

In a smaller market garden, manual wheeled hoes (eg Planet Junior) can be very effective. If you have a good labour force you can use hand hoes. It is beneficial to hoe early in the morning, when the dew can be incorporated into the soil.

Remember that the important thing is to hoe before you need to hoe. The job can be done twice as quickly before your crop is threatened with smothering by weeds.

Another technique, of limited value, is pre-emergence flame weeding: a flame of butane is passed over the seedbed before germination to scorch off the newly germinated weed plants. In this way weeds can be eliminated, for example from a carrot or onion patch, before germination of the crop. However, use of this technique once the crop itself has germinated would be difficult.

One of the best methods of weed control is rotation; for example, regular growing of green crops and returning to pasture. Continual cultivations of one area will often lead to mineral deficiencies, and weeds will grow to try to correct these deficiencies.

An interesting weed-control method is to cultivate the soil lightly at the time when the moon is in the constellation of Leo. This constellation encourages the growth of all seedling plants — good and bad. As the weed seeds germinate, they can be lightly hoed off. This will eliminate the weeds in the top few centimetres of soil and give some relief from weeds for the next crop.

Another aspect to consider is that when you cultivate you bring in the influences of the cosmos. These cosmic influences enter the soil when it is disturbed. Therefore the cultivation of soil and plants at the right time will have great benefit.

*Weeding pumpkins, using a mid-mounted steerage hoe with ducksfeet etc. These undercut the weeds, which are then pulled out by the harrows. A high-clearance, narrow-track tractor is ideal for row crop cultivation*

*Commercial and home vegetable production 117*

## Harvesting

Harvesting should always be done early in the morning to get maximum quality. Root crops should be harvested in a descending period, when the moon is in the constellation of Taurus (an earth constellation). If you are planning to store your vegetables, choose a time when the moon is in Gemini (an air/light constellation). Never harvest at full moon, as there is a high amount of moisture over the earth at that time, and vegetables such as pumpkins will be full of water and will not keep.

## HOME GARDENING

Cultivation times are the same, and the same conditions apply as for market gardening, except that they are scaled down. As the area is more limited it will not be possible to change your garden's situation, so more emphasis must be placed on compost-making, regular green cropping, and a comprehensive crop rotation system (see Table 10.2). Green manures play a very important part in the rotation, in maintaining and improving the soil fertility. They prevent leaching of soil nutrients in the wet winter months, and stimulate biological activity. In autumn, use rye corn and vetch, oats and tick beans or blue lupins. In the summertime use barley and tick beans or similar plants.

In the home garden one of the best methods of crop rotation is to divide the production part of the garden into two parts: one is in crop while the other is growing a continuous green crop or maybe a grass mixture of Italian rye, chicory and clovers for two years. This can be mown regularly, leaving the clippings on the ground. This method will improve the soil structure.

The successful production of vegetables from the home garden plot requires, apart from good soil husbandry and the biodynamic compost, a knowledge of the varieties of plants and their correct sowing or planting time.

Table 10.3 gives sowing and planting times for a few popular vegetables, beginning with the spring garden. The timing is based on the central North Island climate — a temperate climate with moderate summer temperatures and cool winters, and 600–1500ml (25–60in) rainfall. I would suggest where possible, sow at a time when the moon and Saturn are in opposition.

TABLE 10.2: Suggested crop rotation for a home garden

|  | 1997 | | 1998 | | 1999 | | 2000 |
| --- | --- | --- | --- | --- | --- | --- | --- |
| Bed | Autumn | Spring | Autumn | Spring | Autumn | Spring | Autumn |
| 1 | winter veg | roots | WGC[1] | beans & peas | WGC | cabbage salad | WGC |
| 2 | winter veg | SGC[2] | winter veg | roots | WGC | beans & peas | WGC |
| 3 | winter veg | SGC | winter veg | SGC | winter veg | roots | WGC |
| 4 | WGC | SGC | winter veg | SGC | winter veg | SGC | winter veg |
| 5 | WGC | cabbage salad | WGC | SGC | winter veg | SGC | winter veg |
| 6 | WGC | beans & peas | WGC | cabbage salad | WGC | SGC | winter veg |

1 WGC = Winter green crop: ryecorn or oats together with vetch, blue lupins, tick beans
2 SGC = Summer green crop: barley, wheat, oats or buckwheat together with vetch, broadbeans, french beans

*Onions grown for seed*

TABLE 10.3: Home gardener's seed-sowing and planting guide for vegetable growing

| Month | Sow | Plant | Harvest |
|---|---|---|---|
| **July** | Broccoli Fordhook | Aug/Sept | Nov/Dec |
| (under glass) | Cabbage Golden Acre | Aug/Sept | Nov/Dec |
| | Derby Day | Aug/Sept | Nov |
| | Cauli All year round | Aug/Sept | Nov/Dec |
| | Four-Month Phenomenal | Aug/Sept | Nov/Dec |
| | Lettuce Triumph | Aug/Sept | Nov |
| **August** | Broccoli Fordhook | Sept/Oct | Dec/Jan |
| (under glass) | Cabbage Golden Acre | Sept/Oct | Dec/Jan |
| | Derby Day | Sept/Oct | Dec/Jan |
| | Cauli All year round | Sept/Oct | Dec/Jan |
| | Four-Month Phenomenal | Sept/Oct | Dec/Jan |
| | Lettuce Great Lakes | Sept | Nov/Dec |
| | Buttercrunch | Sept | Nov/Dec |
| **September** | | | |
| (under glass) | Cabbage Succession | Nov | Jan/Feb |
| | Green Acre | Nov | Jan/Feb |
| | Lettuce Great Lakes | Oct | Dec |
| | Buttercrunch | Oct | Dec |
| | Oak Leaf | Oct | Dec |
| | Tomato Hardicross (dwarf) | Oct/Nov | Jan/Mar |
| | Moneymaker (tall) or own choice | Oct/Nov | Jan/Mar |
| | Celery Utah | Nov | Feb/Mar |
| | Green Peppers Yoyo | Nov | Feb/Apr |
| (outdoors) | Leeks | Jan | Apr/Aug |
| | Onions Pukekohe (long-keeper) | | Dec/Feb |
| | California Red | | Dec/Feb |
| | Carrot Topweight | | Dec |
| | Chantenay | | Dec |
| | Manchester Table | | Dec |
| | Parsnip Hollow Crown | | May/Aug |
| | Spinach | | Oct/Nov |
| | Silverbeet | | Dec/Sep |
| | Red Beet | | Nov/May |
| **October** | | | |
| (under glass) | Celery Utah | Jan | May/Aug |
| (outdoors) | Cabbage Savoy-type | Jan | May/Aug |
| | Brussels sprouts | Jan | May/Aug |

*120  Commercial and home vegetable production*

| | | | |
|---|---|---|---|
| | Curly kale | Jan | May/Aug |
| | Lettuce Great Lakes | | Dec/Jan |
| | Buttercrunch | | Dec/Jan |
| plus | Dwarf & climbing beans, pumpkin, cucumber, melons, corn | | Jan/Mar |
| | Carrot Topweight | | Jan/Mar |
| | Chantenay | | Jan/Mar |
| | Manchester Table | | Jan/Mar |
| | Parsnip Hollow Crown | | May/Aug |
| | Spinach | | Nov/Dec |
| | Silverbeet | | Dec/Sep |
| | Red beet | | Dec/Jan |
| **November** | Cabbage Savoy-type | Jan | Apr/Jul |
| (outdoors) | Curly kale | Jan | May/Jul |
| | Lettuce Great Lakes | | Jan/Feb |
| | Buttercrunch | | Jan/Feb |
| | Parsley | | Jan/Jul |
| | Beans, corn, melons, courgettes, carrots, beetroot | | Jan/Mar ... Mar/Jul |
| **December** | Cabbage Winter Cross | Feb | May/Jun |
| (outdoors) | Cauli White Acre | Feb | May/Jun |
| | Broccoli Shogun | Feb | Apr/Jun |
| | Lettuce Great Lakes | | Jan/Feb |
| | Buttercrunch | | Jan/Feb |
| | Corn — last sowing | | Mar |
| | Carrot | | Apr/Jul |
| **January** | Cabbage Winter Cross | Mar | Jun/Aug |
| (outdoors) | Cauli White Acre | Mar | Jun/Aug |
| | Broccoli Shogun | Mar | Jun/Aug |
| | Lettuce Great Lakes type | | Feb/Mar |
| | Buttercrunch | | Feb/Mar |
| | Mignonette | Mar | Apr/May |
| | Cos | Mar | Apr/May |
| **February** | Cabbage Winter Cross | end Mar | Jul/Sep |
| (outdoors) | Cauli White Acre | end Mar | Jul/Sep |
| | Broccoli Shogun | end Mar | July/Sep |
| | Lettuce Mignonette | end Mar | Apr/May |
| | Cos | end Mar | Apr/May |
| | Spinach | | Apr/May |
| **March** | Spinach | | Apr/May |
| **April** | Broadbeans | | Sep/Oct |
| | Spinach | | Jun/Jul |

*Tomatoes grown biodynamically*

## Home garden compost

Making and tending your compost heap should be high on the list of autumn and winter jobs: either turning your existing heap or using all the materials you have gathered to make a new one. Your heap should be piled together loosely, keeping everything moist, and mixing the animal manure with the other organic materials from your clean-up. Remember your heap should get quite hot. You can make your heap either in a compost bin or using the windrow system (see notes on compost-making in chapter 6).

1  Materials particularly suited for home garden composts are:
- kitchen scraps
- lawn clippings
- chopped or mulched prunings (eg hedges, fruit trees, roses)
- blood and bone
- rock phosphate

Bin-type compost can be built up gradually as material becomes available. Make in batches weekly or fortnightly to encourage heat process. Cover with damp jute sacks or old carpet during building. You will need two bins — one for the finished compost and one for the compost in the process of being made — and an area for the storage of new compost materials.

Add biodynamic compost preparations when the heap or batch is finished being built. Compost is ready when it breaks down easily between finger and thumb and can be moulded into a shape. In most cases, a barrowload spread over 6 square metres is sufficient.

# ELEVEN

# Calcium and silica

 Rudolf Steiner gives a clue as to the importance of these two elements in his Agricultural Lectures. He points out frequently that an important aim in biodynamic agriculture is to bring about a balance between the calcium and the silica.

## Characteristics

Generally calcium, or limestone as it is commonly known, is beneficial for the successful growing of many crops, although it is not known exactly why. An overuse of limestone rock can oxidize organic matter or the humus with a temporary increase of fertility but with the loss of humus which will lead eventually to soil degradation.

In nature, pure calcium carbonate has a tendency to make varied forms which we see in the wide variety of the seashells. Other examples are seen in stalactites and stalagmites and in the bones of mammals and fish.

Conventional science says very little about silica except that it occurs generally on the skin or the bark of most living things. Some of these plants have very tough, thorny bark and spiny leaves — gorse, for example, and some of the hard thistles. An unusual plant is the equisetum or horsetail, which contains much silica in a living form. Equisetum does not appear to have silica so much on the surface of the leaf, but when the leaves are burnt they leave a skeleton or framework of silica in the ashes. The casuarina, or Australian sheoak, will do the same thing.

In nature, silica occurs in hard rocks and various compound minerals, and in its purest form as silicon oxide where we see it as a clear quartz crystal.

The calcium structure which shows itself in the forms of shells and bones is relatively soft and less permanent than the hard crystal of quartz. Seashells or eggshells will break very easily, whereas quartz needs to be broken up with strong blows of a hammer. Perhaps the form and the substance expressed in these two minerals show how the processes work in nature.

Steiner says that the calcium force in the earth comes from the planets closer to the sun — the moon, Mercury and Venus; while those planets further out than the earth from the sun — Mars, Jupiter and Saturn — bring in the silica influences.

## Processes

A natural process could be described as what brings about anything you see in nature. We don't actually see the process working, but we see the final result, whether it is a crystal, a plant, an animal or a human being. These processes are still not well understood, and various theories have been advanced to try to explain what happens.

For example, look at the shell formation of an egg. In 1972 a French scientist, Louis Kevran, suggested that the calcium content of a chicken egg was directly connected not to the calcium in the hen's diet, but rather to the hen's ability to combine potassium and hydrogen in its food to form the calcium needed for the shell (see Harold Willis 1985, *The Coming Revolution in Agriculture*, pp 181, 182). This calcium-forming activity can be described as a calcium process.

The shell formation of molluscs is a similar process. Sea water does not appear to contain sufficient calcium for the shell: its formation is dependent on a calcium process from the cosmos, working through the water.

Steiner pointed out that the limestone processes are connected to the form of plants, the shape of their leaves, fruit etc, and important-ly, their seeding and reproduction.

Where limestone is present in the soil, earthworm activity increas-es; there is a limestone process within the gut of the earthworm. The nodulation on all legume roots also increases in the presence of limestone, as do the various soil bacteria.

The silica processes, in contrast, are connected to the building up of the substance of the plant, namely the part we eat. They are there to help the building up of starches, sugars and proteins in the plant.

Bearing all the above in mind, how do we go about enhancing the balance between the calcium and the silica on a farm under bio-dynamic management?

## Practical considerations

Preparation 500 is made from dung from a lactating cow, which will have many of the processes of calcium coursing through its metabolic system. It is reasonable to suppose that those calcium energies will be contained in the dung. So when we spray our land with 500 we are bringing the calcium processes into the soil. This is borne out by on-farm observations of the increases in earthworm activity and legume nodulation as mentioned above, and the increase in humus with resultant improvements in soil structure.

The use of Preparation 501 (horn silica) is an obvious way of bringing the silica processes onto the farm. When 501 is used where the 500 has already been working, there is a noticeable improvement in plant health and nutritional quality, and in stock health. The use of these two sprays containing the inherent qualities of these two minerals works towards the balancing of their activity in the soil.

If we consider the planetary influences, we can see that these can be used as well to reinforce the calcium–silica processes. When studying a planting calendar we can observe various planetary connections. One of these is the opposition of the moon and Saturn — that is, when these two planets are on opposite sides of the earth. The moon, being closer to the sun, brings in calcium processes (form), and Saturn, being furthest away from the sun, brings the silica processes (substance). Now if seeds are sown at the time when the moon and Saturn are in opposition, the plant gathers the balance from these two influences into itself, bringing great strength and quality to the resulting growth of the plant. I have observed this effect time after time over the past 28 years.

So to complement the use of Preparation 500 we spray the silica Preparation 501 on the plants. Preparation 501 brings to the plant very much what is happening in the constellations, so when it is sprayed at the time of moon/Saturn opposition, again the balancing of the calcium and limestone takes place.

Just one more observation to think about. Preparation 505 made from oak bark is high in lime, and Preparation 506 made from dandelion is strong in silica processes. Here is another possibility to bring about this balance when using compost and cowpat pit or liquid manures.

## Clay in relation to calcium and silica

Rudolf Steiner makes several references to clay, in relation to silica and calcium, in his Agriculture course. On page 31 of *Agriculture* he states 'What is collected down below from the cosmos (via the silica) must always be able to stream upward, and the presence of clay in the soil makes this possible. Substances like clay support the upward flow of the effects of the cosmic entities in the ground.' Again on page 31, 'All the forces and fine homoeopathic substances produced by means of water and air above the ground are drawn down by the soil's greater or lesser content of lime. It is the lime in the soil and the presence of calcareous substances in homoeopathic doses just above the soil's surface that serve to draw this terrestrial factor into the ground.' On page 33 he says, 'if we are dealing with a soil that does not carry these influences upward during the winter as it should, it is good to furnish the soil with some clay, the dosage of which I will indicate later.' (To my knowledge Steiner never did give the indications of the amount of clay.) And further on page 60 he says, 'and clay mediates between them (silica and limestone). Clay is closer to silica but it still mediates towards lime.'

These comments suggest that in working with biodynamic agriculture we should somehow include clay into our management system. Clays are formed from various rocks containing aluminium silicates that are well weathered. Such materials as feldspar, bentomite or basalt are well known and can be used.

Clay is used as one of the ingredients in the tree paste, which incidently is made from sand or diotomaceous earth (silica) cow dung (calcium) and clay or bentomite (clay) (see pp102–103). Basalt dust is used in the making of the cow pat pit. (See pp63, 65.) Any of these rock dusts can be sprinkled through the compost heap.

Some biodynamic practitioners are experimenting with filling cow horns with clay and burying them in a similar way to making 500 cow horn dung, or making 501 horn silica to activate the clay process. The best time for burying and applications is yet to be determined. I mention this so that practitioners can find their own way with these recently realised indications. Early biodynamic work in Europe in making the Preparations 500 and 501 apparently included a plug of clay in the bottom of the horn. This does seem to make sense in the light of Rudolf Steiner's comments regarding the importance of the clay.

*TWELVE*

# A guide to practical observations

 As soon as I walk onto a farm I can tell if it is being farmed properly according to biodynamic principles. On a biodynamic farm, there is a sense of life, of health, of balance. There is a particular smell — of the cows' breath, of the dung. Other biodynamic farmers have observed this as well. Walk into a cowshed during milking: on a biodynamic farm you will notice settled, quiet cows, pleasant-smelling dung, sweet-smelling milk in the vat, and an unstressed farmer happy in his or her job. Good powers of observation are of great importance in animal and crop husbandry.

## Assessment of pasture and crop quality

A good-quality pasture on good soil will recover quickly after drought. But you don't have to wait for a drought to assess your pasture quality. At any time you can read what the pasture is telling you. It should have an upright nature — particularly the clovers — and have a firm look and a healthy green colour.

In pastures that are more than 10–12cm long, the grass and clover stems should be green with chlorophyll right down to the base. If soluble fertilisers have been put on the pasture, the base of the stems will be white.

To test the grass quality, see how easily you can pull a blade apart. You can learn to gauge the tensile strength. Grass with low tensile strength is low in fibre, and cows need a good fibre content. If the grass feels soft, it has been over-manured.

You can also chew the grass to assess its fibre content, and to see if it tastes sweet or bitter. Exercise some caution with this test — there may be worm eggs on the grass, particularly on a badly managed farm.

You can learn to distinguish from the taste of brassicas whether a plant is sweet or whether it has the bitterness associated with overuse of nitrogen during growth. Brassicas are good indicators of the extent of biodynamic activity in the soil, and the extent to which the nitrogen has been mineralised. Unmineralised nitrogen taken up in the nitrite form will make the brassicas taste bitter.

Assessing when to cut hay is important. It should be done on a light/air day to ensure better leaf preservation. Hay and silage that has been sprayed with Preparation 501 prior to cutting has a unique fragrance — you can smell that 501 has been used.

All biodynamic farmers should cultivate their sense of smell, in order to recognise many biodynamic processes. The skills developed will serve as well as any laboratory. I remember the time when Dr Herbert Koepf visited New Zealand. I took him for a walk in the bush between Tauranga and Rotorua. Herbert picked a fern frond that was decomposing and smelled it. 'Ah, *Bactidiomyces*,' he exclaimed. If you keep practising, you will be able to smell the presence of bacteria and other things.

The sense of smell can also be used to assess the quality of milk or vegetables or sheep dung. I can tell by smelling some compost whether it has had biodynamic compost preparations added to it or not. You can check the quality of the 500, liquid manure and cowpat pit by smelling them.

### Animal characteristics

A good understanding of the basic characteristics of each animal type assists in the understanding of their place on the farm and the conditions they need. Observe a cow lying down chewing her cud. See how she seems to belong near the earth; she almost sinks into it, and gets up with difficulty. Compare her with birds flying — they seem to be ruled by levity; the cow by gravity. The cow relates strongly to the earth, whereas sheep are less settled — they are orientated more towards the light. Horses are different again — like the wind. These characteristics affect the character of the manure which each animal produces.

A cow complements the look of a paddock — she belongs there, in a way that sheep, goats and deer do not. Sheep and goats belong on the hills, where there are shrubs to browse. When sheep are kept in meadows they tend to have health problems such as footrot, scouring and worms, and they grow too fat. Horses belong on the plains. Pigs belong in forests, where they root and forage. If you take an animal away from its natural environment it will tend to become ill. For further discussion of animal characteristics, see Steiner 1970, *Man as Symphony of the Creative Word*; also Koenig, *Man and the Domestic Animal*.

It is interesting to watch what plant species cows eat when you put them into a new paddock. Such observations are useful when deciding what species you should sow.

Your senses can be sharpened to observe all kinds of natural events which you may not have noticed before, and which help you to understand more about plants and animals and how they grow. Have you ever noticed that at sunrise and at sunset the air seems to get colder? At those times there is movement of water and air in and out of the earth. This movement brings the cooling effect.

You will find that your sense of smell and observational skills will improve over the years just as your farm will improve over time. The results of biodynamic management are impressive, but don't expect them to be instant.

# THIRTEEN

# Biodynamic farming on the move — some practical examples

 Nowhere in the world is farming an easy task, be it growing apples, mangoes, corn, rice, vegetables, sheep, goats or cows. It will always be a task that demands the expertise of the farmer who, with skilful management of the farm and use of biodynamic techniques, makes a success of growing the crop. There is a tremendous joy in the growing of such a crop and in knowing that the people who eat it will be well nourished, and that this has been done without harming the environment.

The application of sound biodynamic methods will very much increase the success of the crop being grown; in fact, as the years of using the biodynamic preparations roll by, the successes far outweigh the disappointments.

I have noticed throughout the world at biodynamic gatherings there is a cheerfulness and positivity that one does not experience at other gatherings of farmers. Biodynamic farmers will always share their knowledge and new ideas about this way of agriculture, and this creates a sense of community and the quiet feeling that things are going well down on the farm.

And there are many stories about things going well on the farm and in the orchard. What follows is an account of some farms that have either full Demeter or trans-Demeter certification. In each case the farmers and orchardists are experienced and good operators.

Note: in all the following examples, phosphate in the form of rock phosphate and agricultural limestone is applied only where it is perceived that the land needs it.

## Dairy farm

A dairy farm which has been under biodynamic management for 10 years in the north of New Zealand is running 200 cows on 200 acres.

There is a regular application of Preparation 500 twice a year along with seaweed liquid manure made with Preparations 502–507. The 500 is mixed using a Jaerna model Virbela flowform and is applied by tractor with a 450-litre spray rig.

The cowshed effluent is run through the flowforms with Preparations 502–507 being added in the form of the cowpat pit before it is spread over the pasture with a travelling irrigator (see chapter 7).

There is good pasture growth during most of the year with mixed herbage and a strong clover growth. Adequate conservation of silage and hay is made each year. The soil structure is well formed, with roots penetrating deep into the soil, good clover nodulation and an active earthworm population. The stock are all healthy and there is little call for the services of the vet. Animal deaths on this farm are 1–2 per cent. It is interesting that stock health is noticeably better than on neighbouring farms using conventional farming methods. Overall production of milk is on a par with the district average, and because of the lower inputs — no fertilisers, less spent on animal health and cow replacements for a variety of reasons — this farm is economically sound.

### Sheep and beef farm #1

This farm is on the east coast of the North Island of New Zealand. It is 1800 acres of hilly to rolling country and runs 2000 ewes and 300 cattle of mixed ages. The preparations have been applied for 10 years.

Preparation 500 is applied twice a year in the spring and autumn. Because of the large area of this farm the only practical way to apply the preparations and liquid manures is by helicopter. The 500 is mixed in the large capacity flowform VB500 which can mix 2500 litres easily in one hour. This amount of liquid is sufficient to keep the aircraft operating. Because of the size of this farm the amount of water and Preparation 500 used per acre has been reduced to half of what is normally used: 25g of 500 in 13 litres of water is spread over two acres instead of one. This rate is not recommended for small farms.

The effectiveness of this method of application is borne out by the obvious results in soil quality and in animal health. The soil is of very good structure showing the typical nutty crumbly particles. The grass roots are deep and the farm does not dry out to the extent that other farms in the district do. Earthworm activity is very good with all the cowpats being incorporated into the soil in a short time.

The cattle look brilliant and are in good health and shining, with little or no use of drenches. Only the lambs are drenched, with herbal drenches of garlic and cider vinegar. There is no fly-strike on sheep on this farm (this is a terrible problem on most farms in this part of the world). I am sure this is because the good quality pasture results in good quality dung which does not attract the blowfly in the same way as chemically fertilised pasture does. Also, the animals are more healthy and do not attract many flies.

### Sheep and beef farm #2

This farm is a smaller unit of 300 acres in central Hawke's Bay on the east coast of the North Island of New Zealand. It is on moderately hilly to rolling country with a heavy clay loam soil. The farm carries 11.6 stock units per hectare.

The farm has been under biodynamic management for 12 years. Preparation 500 has been applied regularly twice a year, along the applications of liquid fish manure and liquid seaweed.

The heavy nature of the soil has changed noticeably over this time when compared with the conventionally managed farm next door. The roots go much deeper into the soil, there is a wonderful mixing of the subsoil and the topsoil by the earthworms at a depth of 30cm (12in) or more, which has increased the living topsoil layer. There is good clover nodulation.

The pasture where the land has been flat enough to work up and resow in herbal ley is very good. One paddock of chicory and red clover is exceptional in terms of the bulk and quality of fodder grown. The rest of the farm on the hilly parts is growing mostly rye, white clover and native grasses, which are also an indication of the quality one expects from soils where the preparations are used. It is interesting to note that in all pastoral farms under biodynamic management, farmers report that stock appear to be satisfied with less fodder while still making the same weight gain or making milk. It has been shown (MacGregor pers. comm. 1996) that biodynamically grown grass has a greater dry-matter content than chemically grown grass.

Stock health is good and successful use is made of herbal drenches for young stock.

Because this farm is quite small by New Zealand standards, to support a family the decision was made to add value to its products. Using the market advantage of the Demeter certification, they sell the lamb and beef locally at a premium. The Romney wool is spun into yarn and handknitted into jerseys and baby clothes, and machine knitted into socks, hats and gloves. This wool is soft and knits up beautifully.

## Mixed cropping farm

This farm is in north Canterbury in the South Island of New Zealand. It is 400 acres of flat alluvial soil and a block of 400 acres of hill country which is not all Demeter. On the flats there are 100 acres under crops; wheat, oats, rye, and barley as well as lentils. The farm runs 1000 stock units of cattle and 1000 stock units of sheep over both areas.

The pastures are mostly mixed herbal, having been resown at the end of the rotation of the cropping. The cattle play a very important part in the maintenance of the fertility of the land. They are overwintered on a pad, and the dung and litter is composted and put back onto the paddock.

Preparation 500 is applied twice a year in late spring and early autumn over the flat 400 acres and on the flat and rolling areas of the hills. Cowpat pit manure made with Preparations 502–507 is applied over the farm regularly. Preparation 501 is applied to the grain and lentil crops at the beginning of the growth and just before harvesting. The preparations are applied with tractor and spray rig.

Animal and plant health is good.

The main thrust of this operation is the supplying of processed farm produce to the people who want to eat Demeter-quality food. The wheat, barley and rye are milled into flour on the farm and the oats are rolled. Fat lambs and beef are sold as certified organic on the local market.

## Market garden

This property is 10 acres in South Canterbury and has been under biodynamic management for 15 years. At any one time there would be approximately five acres under crop or green manure; the remainder would be in pasture and have cattle grazing on it. Two or three cows are kept on an overnight pad and the manure is collected each morning for compost-making. Herbs and vegetables are grown; the vegetables are those which are suitable for the district, which is well known for its brussels sprouts, carrots, onions, and potatoes.

Compost is made regularly using the cow manure from the yard,

crop wastes, and hay cut from the property. The compost preparations are added to the compost pile when the heap is completed. The
compost-making in this garden has developed over the years to a
very high standard. Compost is applied at the rate of 20 tonnes per
acre to brassica and potato crops; onions and carrots get less (about
10 tonnes per acre). Seaweed liquid manure made with Preparations
502–507 is applied at least once a month as a tonic.

This market garden pays great attention to using the cosmic
rhythms in all its gardening operations, with great success.

Preparation 500 is applied twice in the year — in the spring when
the soil is warmed up (during the descending period of the moon and
in the afternoon), and again in the early autumn at the descending
period of the moon. Preparation 501 is sprayed on the crops in the
early morning close to harvest time when Saturn is in opposition to
the moon. The seeds are sown generally at the moon/Saturn opposition, making use of the information in the BioDynamic Association's
*BioDynamic Farming and Gardening Calendar*. Harvesting is done at the
appropriate time according to the calendar.

The produce from this market garden is of very high quality and
the taste is superb. It is sold as Demeter in the South Island.

A final note about the soil: it is improving year by year even
though it is being cropped. With careful attention to composting,
green manuring, crop rotations, sensitive cultivation, regularly
returning the land back to pasture, and applying Preparation 500, the
soil humus and the depth of the soil are increasing.

## Citrus orchard

This is a citrus orchard in the Northland region of New Zealand,
growing oranges and tamarillos. It is 10 acres, fully planted with
plenty of space between rows. It has been biodynamically managed
for 10 years.

Preparation 500 is used twice a year. Compost and seaweed liquid
manure made with Preparations 502–507 are used once a month. A
very good sward of white clover and kikuyu grass has been developed, which grows very vigorously and is mown regularly; the mow-
ings provide a wonderful mulch. The weeds around the trees are
dealt with by hand once or twice a year.

It is interesting to note that the growth and vigour of the sward
goes beyond the boundary of the orchard over into the neighbour's
orchard for 30 metres or more, until it gradually stops. This is a phe-

nomenon that is repeated in most places where Preparation 500 is used — the neighbouring land alongside the boundary shows the soil improvement typically associated with the use of this preparation.

The fruit is of very high quality, sweet, keeps well, and sells well.

### Avocado-growing

This is not an observation of a specific orchard, but after visiting several biodynamic orchards I have come up with the following.

Avocados grow quite well in the warmer places of New Zealand where it is frostfree and there is good soil drainage. They are very easy to grow under biodynamic management and the use of the full range of preparations makes for good-tasting fruit. Leaf mould builds up under the canopy of the bigger trees, into which the feeding roots will run. This will happen only where no chemical weed sprays have been used under the trees.

Compost application is very important, as avocados are gross feeders. It should be applied liberally under and up to the dripline. Liquid seaweed manure should be sprayed regularly, at least once a month. As the trees reach large proportions a special spray rig will be needed for this task.

There are however a few problems that occur in avocado growing. After about 10–12 years all the trees of this age throughout the growing areas, biodynamic or conventional, are dying back. There are several theories as to why. One suggested cause is the root fungus phytophthera. When the tree begins to age and the roots become less vigorous, they are killed by the fungus. This is, I think, a secondary problem due to lack of vigour.

Another theory is that only the variety Hass is affected; all other varieties seem to be able to cope. Unfortunately Hass is the most popular variety grown.

Yet another theory is that, because the trees have been planted so close, there has been a heavy demand on nutrition and no nutrients are left in the soil to support growth. The trees become less vigorous, and the roots are then attacked by the phytophthera root fungus as previously mentioned.

This last theory seems the most likely: I have seen health return to the trees when the tree is cut back to stimulate new growth, and masses of compost and mulch is put around the dripline to encourage the young feeding roots which reappear.

In another instance, a very heavy dressing of seaweed meal was worked into the soil around the dripline of one of a group of trees that had lost most of their leaves. With this boost of fertiliser, the leaves came back, while the other trees that were not treated with any seaweed did not recover.

Obviously this die-back problem is a classic case of a monoculture gone wrong. To grow the avocado biodynamically one should first look for natural companion plants. Plant a mixed subtropical orchard and maintain the fertility of the land right from the beginning with composts and mulches, and use all the preparations in the ways mentioned in this book to maintain and sustain the fertility.

### Grape-growing for raisin production

This vineyard is in Fresno, California, near the foothills of the Sierra Mountains. The main crops grown in this district are almonds and grapes. The vineyard covers 50 acres and is surrounded by conventional growers. The soil is very light and of a sandy nature, washed down from the granite mountains. There is very little humus. The area is flood-irrigated once a month. The variety of grapes grown is Thompson's Seedless. The climate is mild, ranging from a slight winter chill to extremely hot summer temperatures, which makes for good raisin production.

This vineyard has been biodynamic for four years. Preparation 500 has been applied twice a year and sometimes more often, with monthly sprayings of Preparation 501 during the growing season. A stirring machine is used, and a tractor spray rig for application.

Compost is applied over half the orchard each year. The compost is made from brought-in cow manure and straw or old hay and goes through a hot fermentation process with Preparations 502–507 added. Seaweed manure is applied during the growing season. A green manure crop of oats, blue lupin and vetch is grown after harvest in alternate rows and disced in before bud break. Weeding is done by cultivation.

The vineyard is showing some very noticeable differences from the neighbouring vineyards which are chemically fertilised, chemically weeded and chemically sprayed for pests and diseases. The soil structure is very much improved. The growth of cane for next year's crops is strong, internodes are close but well spaced for a good crop compared with the neighbouring vineyard where the nitrogen-boosted plants have widely spaced internodes. The good cane growth is due to the 501 sprayings, and there is a very low incidence of insect attack on leaves. Production is better than average, and most importantly, the superior taste of the raisins is widely acclaimed.

### Mango-growing
These orchards are in the South of India in the district of Madurai in the foothills of the Palni Hills near Kodaikanal.

There are several orchards with a total of 1500 acres being managed biodynamically for the past two years, although the first orchard of 150 acres was converted four years ago. It was the success of the management of this orchard that inspired other growers to do the same.

This orchard dehydrates all the fruit in a solar-heated factory on one of the farms. Other fruits such as bananas, pineapples and pears are also dried and are sold on the German market.

Preparation 500 is sprayed at least twice a year and 501 at least once. These preparations are all stirred by hand. The 500 is also applied by hand with a brush but the 501 is sprayed in mist above the trees using a pump and a nozzle on the end of a long wand.

There has been a tremendous amount of compost made from crop wastes, factory wastes from the dehydrating plant, cow-dung slurry,

*Spraying 501 on mangoes*

*138 Practical examples of biodynamic farming*

reservoir tank silt, and coconut fibre. The compost is applied regularly around the dripline of the trees, and liquid manure sprays are made from neem leaves, cow manure, cow urine, and from the foliage of various legume trees. The cowpat pit is applied over all the orchard as a liquid foliar spray.

The farm is managing a block of pear trees in Kodaikanal which is at an altitude of 1800m (6000ft), which at that latitude means a temperate climate. All the preparation herbs grow here, and they are thus able to make all the preparations.

This farm runs comprehensive seminars and field days which are a joy to be a part of. There are wonderful examples of cowhorns, all the preparations and the preparation flowers, cowpat pit, compost and compost heaps.

Because of the work involved this farm employs about 100 people in a wonderful holistic environment, and this of course supports all the employees' families. The social side of biodynamic farming is one of the most important dynamics, where there is a good interaction between people.

*FOURTEEN*

# A journey into India with biodynamics

In the light of the previous chapters I would like to share my experiences working with biodynamic agriculture on the continent of India. This of course is a tropical continent which is vastly different in weather conditions and seasonal changes from that which I had been used to in the temperate countries such as New Zealand and Australia.

What I had to adjust to was the unfamiliar rhythm of the monsoon — to me, a totally new climate that gets all the year's rainfall in the space of two or three months. People then have to get by with no rain for a period of nine months, and crops have to grow through the consequent drought. On top of this, temperatures are extremely hot, averaging 35°C and higher in the summer. There is a little relief in the winter months of December and January when average temperatures plummet to 25°C average, sending people to wrap in their winter woollies. All this is no problem for the local farming population because this has been happening in India ever since India was, but for the *vadeshi* it is very different.

The monsoon, which should come to the western part of India in the middle of June, can be preceded by stifling hot temperatures of up to 45°C and even 50°C on the central plateau. Heavy rains through July and August ease off in September, with a cooling of the temperature. Then the monsoon sweeps up and over to the east to the Bay of Bengal and then returns down the southeastern coast in October and November with a similar temperature pattern.

The challenge was how to adapt to this weather pattern in relation to making the biodynamic preparations. Also, would it be possible to grow the preparation plants, which are from a temperate climate, in such a hot climate? It must be appreciated that all the indications given by Rudolf Steiner were related to middle-European countries. With no model to copy it was just a matter of going ahead and seeing what would happen.

It did seem obvious to start by making the cowhorn dung and to make it in the relatively cool time of the winter (November to February). Now the cow and its dung are highly venerated by the Indian people, so the concept of putting dung into a cowhorn and burying it in the earth struck a sympathetic chord in their farming philosophy. As the Indian proverbs say, 'The Goddess of Prosperity lives in cow dung', and 'In every cow live forty million gods'.

To get the cowhorns was not as easy as one might imagine. As the cow is sacred, most Indian people do not eat meat, so cows are rarely slaughtered. This means that one has to rely on natural death before the horns are available. There are literally millions of cows throughout India so there are always cows dying, and thus there is usually a plentiful supply in the yard where all the dead cows are taken.

Another difference from Western culture is the Indian farmer's custom of painting the cows' horns blue, red, green or yellow on festival occasions or during election times. This paint is usually scraped off before the dung is put into the horn.

### Making the preparations
The first attempt in making the Preparation 500 at the Jawaharlal Nehru Krishi Viswa Vibyala (JNKVV) Agricultural University in Indore on the central plateau in Madhya Pradesh was not at all successful. This was incidentally exactly the same place that Sir Albert Howard in the 1930s made his now famous 'Indore Compost' experiments. But for us it was the beginning of a very steep learning curve. Many wise heads, including Shri TGK Menon, Dr Khosla and Dr Trifale, thought about the problem which revolved around soil fertility and soil moisture. So the following year we used the same location but mixed compost with the existing soil in the pit before burying the horns. Also we mulched quite heavily with paddy straw to keep the pit cool and well moistened during the winter dry period.

This time we were able to lift approximately 60 horns of very good 500 by New Zealand standards, after only four and a half months. Subsequently we have put several hundred horns successfully in other places in the Indore district and also in the south of India in the Madurai district in Tamil Nadu. There, in 1996, we successfully put down and lifted 3000 horns, recovering about 200kg of good cowhorn dung. In Indore we buried a further 26,000 horns. It is interesting to note that those very big horns from the Indian cattle with the large volume of manure that they can contain seem to make

*Some of the 26,000 cowhorns buried near Indore in October 1996*

excellent 500 in the warm climate. All the horns are filled by hand using fingers and thumbs. With the enthusiastic labour available, 3000 horns could be filled in about four hours.

Also at Indore, at the same time as the second attempt at making 500, we made Preparations 502–506 in exactly the same way as they are made in New Zealand (see chapter 7). Again, what about the animal parts that were needed? Well, back to the dead cow yard; and with the aid of Dr Solanki, a retired Ministry of Agriculture vet, we obtained the necessary parts from a young cow that had recently died from eating a plastic bag. The parts had to be used very quickly because of the number of flies and the rapid putrefaction in the extreme heat.

We added compost to the soil again, placed each of the preparations in an earthenware pot, and buried them separately 400mm deep. Just below the surface of the soil we put pieces of thornbush to discourage the wild dogs, and we put compost on top to encourage any worms to go there instead of into the preparation. The skull can be buried in a barrel near an irrigation pond or some wet spot.

All the compost preparations turned out very well and were duly stored in glass jars in a cool spot.

*Filling horns with 500*

We made Preparation 501 relatively easily from local quartz which occurs in geodes in the district around Indore. The quartz is ground to a fine meal in a mortar and pestle, made into a paste and buried in the good soil that has been described previously.

## Soya Bean Trial at Indore Agricultural College

At Indore Agricultural College a trial growing soya beans has been carried out by Dr Khosla, comparing the effects of biodynamic preparations on soil and crop with the effects of conventional chemical fertiliser application. The trial area was divided into four one-acre plots as follows:

Plot 1: treated with locally made 500 together with a small amount of compost made with Preparations 502–506, all of which had been made at Indore, and Preparation 507 from New Zealand

Plot 2: treated with chemical fertiliser of 20N 60P 20K

Plot 3: treated with chemical fertiliser of 10N 30P 10K

Plot 4: the control.

Colour plate 8 shows the improved soil structure, root development and growth in the biodynamic plot 1 compared with the growth

*The experiment showed increased soya bean crop production when both compost and Preparation 500 were used.*

in the chemically fertilised plot 2 and in the control plot 4. No photo was made of plot 3.

The yield of the biodynamic plot 1 was 30 per cent higher than any of the other plots.

Another trial in the following season, this time using wheat, showed very similar results in relation to the soil structure and crop growth. It should be pointed out that the 500 had been sprayed just four months before the start of the trial.

### Growing the preparation plants in India

I found that it was impossible to grow the preparations plants in the hot climate of the central plateau. As luck would have it, Kurinji Farms in the south, which grow mainly mangoes, have a pear orchard in the hills at 2000m, which has a much cooler temperature range than on the plains. Here we found dandelion and yarrow growing, and we introduced chamomile and nettle. Valerian is yet to be established but it is only a matter of time before that happens. The difficult one is the European oak: the only specimens are moss-covered and very weak-looking.

However, in the very north of India, in the foothills of the Himalayas around Nainital, we found an evergreen oak (*Quercus*

*Growing the legume sun hemp as green manure in southern India*

*dilatata)* which has a very high calcium content in its bark, almost twice the percentage of *Q. robur*. We also found a perennial nettle *(Urtica parviflora)* which looks promising.

With both these areas in the north and the south it looks as if it will be possible to grow the plants we require for preparation-making. Biodynamic preparations can then be made in sufficient quantities to enable widespread adoption of biodynamic management in India.

# FIFTEEN

# Biodynamic farming elsewhere

 Biodynamic agriculture has been practised in many European countries since Rudolf Steiner gave his Agriculture Lectures in 1924; and Ehrenfried Pfeiffer took the impulse to the United States in the early 1950s. Biodynamic preparations were first applied in New Zealand in 1928.

The whole development of the technology of the biodynamic approach has taken place largely in the temperate zones of the world, perhaps with the thought that it would not be applicable to tropical or arid regions (presumably because Steiner did not mention tropical or arid countries in his lectures).

A great library of experience, both practical and theoretical, has been developed over the past 70 years in European countries, especially Germany, Holland, Switzerland and Sweden. Most countries have looked to Germany for a lead in this development — it is considered the cradle of the impulse for biodynamic agriculture. I have personally learned and gained a tremendous amount from giants of the movement such as Dr Herbert Koepf, who has written books and instigated informative scientific experiments on the subject (see Koepf 1987, *The Biodynamic Farm*).

Another leading light is Maria Thun, who from her farm in Germany has with great single-mindedness of research spanning 40 years or more, pointed out to the agricultural world the effects of the cosmic workings in every thing growing. Her *Work ing on the Land and the Constellations* is written in such a way that farmers can use the basic information she gives to plan their own planting, sowing and harvesting times and to develop systems to suit the conditions on their farm.

Dr Jochen Bockemuhl, from the Natural Science Section of the Goetheanum in Switzerland, has presented a wonderful gift to students of the agricultural world with his observations of nature and studies of the metamorphosis of plants. His book, *In Partnership with*

*Nature*, (1981) opened up for me a whole new world of observations of plants and their connections with the cosmos, which is an integral part of the study of biodynamic agriculture.

Over the years in Germany, valuable work has been done in the making and the use of the preparations. Scientific experiments have also been carried out, and this has helped the credibility of the movement as well as the practical work of farmers (see Koepf, *The Biodynamic Farm*). The Demeter certification trademark set up in Germany in 1928 was the first production standard to be set up in the world, and one on which subsequent standards have been modelled.

I have visited quite a few biodynamic farms in Sweden, Holland, Austria, Switzerland and Germany; and there are farms in most other European countries as well. Generally the farms are smaller than those in the southern hemisphere, and probably make more intensive use of the land than New Zealand farms do. European farms typically run a produce shop which the farmer stocks with a wide range of goods such as flour, wholemeal bread, cheeses, quark, yoghurt, butter, milk, meats and small goods, all seasonal vegetables, fruits and berries, as well as fruit juices from other farms, so customers can buy nearly all their food there, and all of Demeter quality. What a joy! — but what a pity they are not in every town in every country of the world.

There is now in Europe a growing awareness of the dangers posed by agricultural chemicals in the pollution of the environment. The organic agricultural movement as such is growing in popularity and people are looking for 'residue free' products in the marketplace. Unfortunately most farmers are turning not to the biodynamic method but rather to the 'organic' methods that were practised in the 1920s. I hope this book has convinced the reader of the need to convert farms, not only to an organic system, but to the added dimension of biodynamics. I feel that there needs to be a renaissance not only in Europe but throughout the world, to present this new direction in agriculture to people everywhere.

We are now going through the changing of the guard. The pioneers are no longer there, and as always, there is a gap before the next generation takes over. I have met many farmers of the next generation in Europe: they are confident and enthusiastic, and they can understand the importance of the biodynamic approach and take it on into the future.

## Eastern Europe

The Eastern block of Europe was starved of any biodynamic input during the communist regime. The only work I know of was carried out in Budapest in Hungary during the occupation by Clara Mezei, who made the preparations at home and distributed them secretly to friends for their home gardens. The Hungarian movement is now being established.

After the collapse of communism there have been a number of initiatives in most countries in the East. Poland has had biodynamic farms for more than five years now, and as in Estonia, Latvia and Lithuania, farmers are being helped by advisors from Sweden, Germany and Holland.

Work started in Russia over a decade ago, and since then a number of ventures have been set up with help from German, Canadian and American advisors. In the Ukraine, Moldavia, Georgia and Armenia things are beginning to happen with preparations being made and applied. These countries are being helped by advisors from Germany and America.

## Mediterranean

There is a large group of biodynamic farms in Egypt growing cotton. I understand this is a very enthusiastic and successful venture.

A few small biodynamic farms exist in Israel. Preparations are being made and used in the arid areas of Tunisia; this initiative is being helped by advisors from Holland.

## UK and Ireland

As yet there are very few biodynamic farms in the UK. The ones that are there are good. There has been a strong input there over the years since Steiner gave his original course, with an active biodynamic association working with great enthusiasm making the preparations, running field days and producing a newsletter. There is an active home-garden movement. For a number of years there was a biodynamic agricultural course at Emerson College, but for some reason the impulse has not taken off in mainstream agriculture. It is not as though biodynamics does not work in the UK — there are some excellent examples of farms and gardens in the Camphill Homes throughout Britain, Wales and Scotland; in fact the vegetable gardens are some of the best I have ever seen. (Camphill Homes are communities established to provide spiritual care, along the lines suggested by Rudolf Steiner. They were founded in Scotland shortly before the Second World War by Dr Karl Koenig, an Austrian student of Rudolf Steiner. There are now more than 40 such homes in the UK and at least 50 in other countries throughout the world, and all have biodynamically run gardens and farms.)

Forest Row in Britain is the home of the Virbela flowform design and research. The forms, developed by John Wilkes, are making a tremendous impact on the mixing of biodynamic preparations and liquid manures.

In Ireland there are a few farms and a very enthusiastic and lively association which should soon show positive results.

As with the rest of the world, I think the UK is ready for a biodynamic explosion, orchestrated largely by younger enthusiasts.

## North America

A similar situation exists in the United States. As previously mentioned, Ehrenfried Pfeiffer did a huge amount of work during the 1950s setting up laboratories and research centres. Pfeiffer also developed a compost starter based on the compost Preparations 502–507, which is still in existence, and which was used successfully in Oakland, California to break down municipal garbage wastes from 1950 to 1952 (*Secrets of the Soil*, pp31–36). Unfortunately this impulse was 'leant on' by the fertiliser multinationals of the time and the operation was closed down. This was a great disappointment to Pfeiffer, and it dampened his enthusiasm for continuing the work.

At the present time most of the biodynamic activity in the US is on the west and east coasts; but overall there are relatively few farms, considering the size of the country. The preparation-making which is based in Virginia is of a high standard. There is a well-organised biodynamic association. In Maine there is a Virbela flowform research centre, and a research institute in East Troy in Wisconsin is working on the development of corn varieties and doing experiments on cowpat pit and the uses of preparations and flowforms. But again one wonders why, with the great examples of biodynamic agriculture in this country, there are not more people inspired to 'give it a go'.

In the Dominican Republic there is a very successful biodynamic grower of bananas, whose fruit tastes great and who is running seminars in biodynamic agriculture there.

In Canada there are a few committed farmers and an association with a huge potential for growth. It is tempting to imagine all the wheat in Canada being grown as Demeter, and the benefits to the millions of people who would eat bread made from this wheat.

## South America
There is a biodynamic institute in Brazil at Botucatu which is the centre of a community project initiative. Here is a large mixed farm growing vegetables and herbs and also supplying milk to a milk-processing factory. In the same district there several smaller farms, which are growing maize, beans, rice, vegetables, and grassland for dairy cows. Close by is a Rudolf Steiner school and a cultural centre where biodynamic farmers are trained.

## The Pacific Rim
Work has started on the development of biodynamic farming systems in the Philippines, Japan, Malaysia, Singapore and Hawaii.

## Australia
Robert Williams was the Australian biodynamic pioneer who perfected the preparation-making in the late 1930s and 40s and shared his knowledge with his Australian colleagues and with their New Zealand cousins across the Tasman.

There are now two biodynamic associations in Australia — one in Victoria and the other in northern NSW. Both associations are very active and support a large number of farms throughout the whole of Australia growing a wide range of crops, including grains, fine wool and lambs, beef, subtropical and tropical fruits, nuts, citrus, and a full range of vegetables and herbs. The Australian farming scene is very diverse, with growing conditions ranging from tropical country in the north growing crops such as bananas, to arid outback sheep-country, to highly productive market gardens and orchards on the eastern coast and in the south.

Biodynamic agriculture has reached a high level of expertise over the years, with both associations making good quality preparations to distribute to their members. They also offer advisory services. There are regular field days and seminars, especially in the eastern areas. Many farms are encouraged to make their own Preparation 500, with emphasis on quality.

This brief summary of biodynamic activity around the world gives some idea of how widespread this impulse is. It is small as yet; but as always, a seed must be sown before a tree can grow.

# SIXTEEN

# Conclusion: why biodynamic agriculture?

 Biodynamic agriculture is a system of organic agriculture that has proved to be very effective throughout the world. The results are better soils, quality food, healthy plants, healthy and contented animals, and enthusiastic farmers and consumers.

It's not as if it's a fly-by-night idea that has no basis for reality. It's happening and has been for 70 years!

*So what's the problem?*
The world is slowly becoming aware of the problems of pollution facing humanity, particularly in the agricultural field. Entrepreneurs see a market for selling food that has been grown with fewer pollutants, but still with the downstream adverse effects on the environment. There is a growing movement of farmers who are genuinely trying to grow organically; but often they are only replacing the chemical inputs of the conventional grower with organic inputs. It is still the same basic understanding of growing: input = output.

In contrast, biodynamic techniques enhance, rejuvenate, add to and maintain soil quality. Cowhorns and cow dung, after being buried together in the earth, make the most wonderful humus to spread on the land. This improves the structure of the soil dramatically and quickly. Good soil structure means better water-holding capacity, which means better control, with consequently less loss of topsoil, which means better and deeper roots and less need for irrigation, which means deeper soil and more natural fertility.

We know that the earth is tired and overstressed. People have been taking and taking for years and not putting anything back. Now, through biodynamic farming, we have the chance to change this.

*So what's the problem?*

1 Cowhorns — people don't understand what these have to do with growing crops.
2 Because this concept is different from what is considered the norm, people think it must therefore be wrong.
3 People ask, 'How can such a small amount have such an effect? Have you had it scientifically tested?'

## Earth fertility and food quality

The farmers of India have no problem in understanding the majesty of the cow in relationship to the continuance of fertility of the earth. They realise the cow is a gift from heaven.

Indian agriculture has a history of 4000 years. Indian farmers recognise the connection of the divine in the growing of food, and have done for years. We in the West prefer to turn our back on help from on high. We think we can do it all ourselves, and that we are the masters of creation.

People of Western cultures are generally interested in quantity of production rather than quality. This is a greedy attitude, but one admired and applauded by the lords of economic performance. When applied to the growing of food, this attitude is justified by the need to feed a hungry world. Unfortunately, it is beginning to rub off on Asian people as well.

*It can be done*

It is possible to grow sufficient food for the world without poisoning our planet. We do not need to use a whole array of chemicals and synthetic materials. The use of hybridised or genetically engineered seeds is totally unnatural and unnecessary (see chapter 10).

Biodynamic technology with its informed use of the various preparations will maintain soil fertility for years to come in a wholly natural way. It will support the growing of a plentiful supply of nourishing food. In India it has been shown that soya beans grown using biodynamic methods produce 30 per cent more crop than those that are chemically grown.

At some point in considering our existence in this world, most people come to a recognition that there is a higher power than ourselves that is responsible for creation; that there is a force of growth, albeit a beneficent one. Nature provides us with examples of this life force every day, in the mighty trees of the forest, in scented roses, a medicinal herb, a nourishing carrot or a blade of grass.

This is where we must grasp the nettle in our attempt to understand biodynamic agriculture and to make the connection between this force of growth and the use of the biodynamic preparations.

The preparations are made from all-natural products — cow dung, quartz, and medicinal herbs — and are processed in conjunction with various animal parts. These preparations when applied to the soil, through ground sprays, composts and liquid manures, enliven the soil. They make happen all the biological soil processes, referred to in chapter 3, that soil scientists talk about but rarely see in the field (see Reganold et al, 1993).

Another thing that biodynamic farmers take into consideration is that the heavenly bodies and the fixed stars in their constellations play a very important role in the continuance of life on our planet. This is the basis of biodynamic agriculture.

Steiner gave the world ideas on a renewal of agriculture. He pointed out that we must nourish the earth in such a way that the cosmic influences could continue to flow in. During his lectures, the idea for the use of the biodynamic preparations was born.

Using the biodynamic preparations regularly opens the soil and the land to the effects of cosmic activities and allows these to work through the soil into the plants. The more biologically active the earth, the more the beneficent forces can work through into plant and animal.

Human beings, consumers of plants and animal products, gain in forces and the capacity to develop their soul life and personal life when eating the food that is grown in this enlivened environment.

These concepts are beautifully simple, logical and easy to understand if people have the right mindset. There are no hidden agendas here. Recognition of this renewal of agriculture has to come about.

It's all about our drinking water — its purity and its quality.

It's about quality food.

It's about the social life on farms all over the world.

It's about an affordable, sustainable system of agriculture that will allow all farmers to stay on their land for many years.

It's about farming being the most important activity in the world.

In my opinion it will only be biodynamic agriculture and all that emanates from it, that can give the world the spiritual hope and confidence for the future that we are all looking for.

*Think about it.*

*APPENDIX ONE*

# Storage and use of the biodynamic preparations

## PREPARATIONS 500 AND 501

### Quantities to use

The stirred preparations are applied at the rate of 13 litres (3 gallons) per acre or 33 litres per hectare. All preparations should be applied within one hour of stirring, so only mix up the amount you can apply in an hour. This amount depends on the method of application and whether you have friends to help.

Multiply the number of acres you can cover in an hour by 13 to find out how many litres of preparation to stir. For example: If you and your friends can walk over 7 acres of land in an hour, then the most preparation to stir at a time is 7 x 13 = 90 litres.

If you can cover 50 acres with a tractor and spray rig per hour, then stir 50 x 13 = 650 litres at one time.

### Stirring equipment and how to stir

*For up to one acre of land*

Up to 13 litres can be comfortably stirred by hand with a small stick. Stir while resting your elbows on your knees. To make a good vortex requires a wristy movement. Start slowly at the edge of the bucket and move into the centre, increasing the stirring speed. When a crater appears in the water, break it by stirring in the opposite direction. You can change hands when changing direction, and it is easier to always stir outward, ie with the right hand clockwise and with the left hand anticlockwise. There should be about three direction changes a minute.

*For 1–10 acres of land*

Up to 130 litres can be stirred using a 200-litre plastic drum or an oak barrel, with a 1.3–1.6m long, 2.5cm diameter wooden rod, suspended by means of a nylon cord tied firmly to an overhanging branch, beam or a tripod of stout poles. The rod is tied so that it is swinging 7cm above the bottom of the barrel. The rod thus takes all the weight and makes the stirring and creating of the vortex relatively easy.

*For 10–200 acres*
A rotating paddle system, driven by a 1Hp electric motor, can be used to stir 140–230 litres — enough to do 10–16 acres at a time. The motor is connected to timing and reversing switch gear, which enables the direction of rotation to alternate just as a hand-stirrer would. The vortex should develop as quickly as possible with this size machine, usually taking 30–45 seconds. There should be a 6 to 10-second delay before the opposite rotation begins. Set the time switch to 30–45 seconds on and 6–10 seconds off.

*For 200–500 acres*
A hydraulic motor is needed to stir 450–1400 litres. The motor is linked up to the hydraulic system of a tractor at 40Hp or more. The reversing and timing switch gear is run off the tractor's 12-volt system.

## Virbela flowforms
There are four types of Virbela flowform cascades available for mixing fertilisers, which are also suitable for stirring Preparations 500 and 501:
  • The Jaerna, which stirs up to 900 litres in an hour
  • The Beehive, which stirs up to 900 litres in an hour
  • The Herten, which stirs up to 1800 litres in an hour
  • The VB500, which stirs up to 2700 litres in an hour
  • The Vortex, which stirs up to 2700 litres in an hour
  The movement that water makes as it passes through the flowform cascade is one of alternating vortices. This is very similar to the succession of vortices produced in a bucket or a barrel while stirring, except that you can see the whole succession laid out in front of you at once. The vortices, however, occur one after another, just as they do in a bucket, because the water flows from a clockwise-rotating chamber into an anticlockwise one, and so on.
  A cascade always has a separate 'entry' form at its head, which sets up the right conditions for water entering the system. With a cascade of 14 Jaerna forms (plus entry form) it is possible to stir up to 900 litres in one hour. With 7–14 (plus one) VB500 forms it is possible to stir up to 2700 litres in one hour. At the moment a high-volume, low-pressure pump is used to circulate the water continuously for an hour. Other pumps with a softer action are being investigated.

*A portable Jaerna flowform used for mixing 500 and liquid manure*

**Water**

Rainwater is preferable and, in areas of little pollution, can be collected off the roofs of houses, woolsheds and hay barns. It can be stored in concrete, galvanised iron or untreated wooden tanks.

If spring water is used, it should be checked for pollutants and chemical residues. If found to be clean, it should stand in the light and air for two days, as it may have been underground for many years. River water should likewise be checked for purity.

**Heating water**

Water for stirring should be between 25° and 30°C, and it is best heated with a natural heat such as a flame or sunlight. Suitable heaters are butane or woodburners and solar panels. An old-fashioned copper or a 44-gallon steel drum over a fire or burner, or a Marshall (Thermette-type) heater are satisfactory.

SPRAYING OF PREPARATION 500

This is best done in the afternoon, in autumn or early spring and while the moon is in a descending phase (see planting calendar). It is best to cover your land in an ingoing spiral, starting from the outside, rather than to zig-zag back and forth.

**Hand application**

For small areas use a hearth brush (not nylon). Dip the brush into the stirred 500, and spread the liquid using an action similar to a backhand tennis stroke with an upward movement as you walk along. This will spread large droplets over a width of about 10 metres.

*156   Appendix 1: Storage and use of preparations*

## Wheeled vehicles

Larger areas of 20 acres or more can be sprayed with a tractor, using a centrally mounted three-jet nozzle, which will give 9–18m of coverage at a pressure of 20–40psi, created by a rotary or diaphragm pump. A long boom spray is too unwieldy, and of no advantage.

Another arrangement is the four-wheel drive farm bike towing a trailer with a 450-litre tank. A centrifugal pump, electrically driven from the bike's battery, provides the spraying power. You can expect such an arrangement to cover 20–30 acres per hour on flat land. On hilly country saddle tanks can be fitted to the bike, using the same pump and nozzle system. It is also possible to fit a spray gun which will reach inaccessible slopes and gullies.

In easy, rolling country a four-wheel drive utility such as a Land Rover can be used. You can mount a 900-litre tank on such a vehicle, with a small petrol motor to drive a diaphragm pump, again with the centrally mounted three-jet nozzle. It is often possible to cover 60–70 acres an hour with such a rig.

Nozzles for spraying Preparation 500 are best mounted low to the ground. There are several sources of suitable jets (Spraying Systems Co. makes one called Boom Jet Nozzle), or you can make your own. The spray gear should be run at a pressure of 20–40psi.

*Boom jet nozzle*

## Aircraft

Aircraft need to have four open-ended nozzles along a boom fixed to each wing or under the helicopter. An air-driven pump feeding off a 900-litre hopper tank completes the arrangement. Since an aircraft can spread 900 litres in about 15 minutes, you need to stir 2700 litres at a time, and store the remaining 1800 litres. The stirring machine or flowform can then be used for mixing the next batch while the first batch is being applied. An 1800-litre black plastic tank is suitable.

You may have noticed that these calculations seem to have 'lost' 15 minutes out of the hour. This time will be used by the operator in loading and taxiing. But if the airstrip is distant from the paddock, you may have to adjust these figures, and stir smaller batches to allow for the increased flying time.

One logistical problem of aerial spraying is the large volume of rainwater needed. For example, for a 1000-acre farm, you will need 13,600 litres (3000 gallons) of water. A bit of thought is necessary to work out a system of water-collection facilities, and cartage by tanker or pipe to the airstrip, and the warming once it is there.

One farmer has an ideal setup. His woolshed, with its large roof catchment area, is quite close to, but higher than the airstrip. Thus, gravitational supply of water to the airstrip is possible. The advantage of using a helicopter is that it does not need a runway, so it can go to where the water is stored and mixed.

It is important that the aircraft spraying system is clean and free of pollutants. (A contaminated tank can be cleaned with bleach, followed by a thorough rinse.) Some farmers form a syndicate which owns the pump, boom and liner for the tank. In the future it is possible that there will be aircraft operators who work only with biodynamic farmers.

SPRAYING OF PREPARATION 501

This is best done early in the morning, in spring during an ascending period of the moon or when the moon and Saturn are in opposition. It can also be done when the crop is almost mature, but spraying 501 while the crop is still developing is likely to cause it to hasten into maturity. This may lead, for example, to beautifully formed but very small lettuces.

When spraying, observe how far the spray mist is carried by any wind movement. You can make the next pass over the garden or paddock at the point that the spray drift has reached. You can adjust your travelling speed according to the wind movement — on a very still morning you will travel or walk back and forth (not spiral) across the land more quickly than on a day when the wind is carrying the spray mist a good distance.

Small areas should be done with a knapsack or motorised knapsack sprayer. Use a fine nozzle and direct the spray up into the air.

Larger areas can be covered using the same machinery as described for spraying Preparation 500. The main differences are that the pressure should be much higher (80–100psi), and the nozzle jets should be changed to a smaller aperture, creating a fine mist which is allowed to drift — wind direction (if not too strong) can be used to advantage.

## GENERAL POINTS ABOUT EQUIPMENT

If you are buying equipment for spraying or stirring preparations, consider other possible uses for it. The most likely use is the mixing or spreading of liquid fertiliser.

Be careful of old or secondhand equipment — you need to be certain it has not been used for herbicides or other agricultural chemicals.

## STORING PREPARATIONS

If the preparations are not used immediately after receiving them, or if you find it more convenient to have a stock on hand, they should be stored in a suitable container to prevent the loss of the vital life forces.

Preparations 502–507 are best placed in small glass jars or glazed earthenware pots with loose-fitting lids. The five jars or pots as well as the bottle of valerian should be stored in a box which is well insulated with peat or sphagnum moss. To make such a box, place a small box within a large one, and pack the peat or sphagnum between the two. The sphagnum should be dry.

The lid of the storage box should be also insulated. For this, use a sandwich construction of peat or sphagnum between two 10mm boards. Make sure the wood used in the box construction is untreated.

Check regularly that the preparations are moist enough, and if not, add a small amount of rainwater — half a teaspoon may be all that is needed in the case of compost preparations. Remember the preparations are living, so they need a little air: do not screw the lids down tight.

When your preparations are well stored they develop a life of their own, and you will notice bacterial deposits like small worm castings on the sides of the jars.

Preparation 500 can be stored in glass jars (eg Agee) or glazed earthenware pots with loose-fitting lids or corks, and placed in a storage box as described above, or surrounded by peat or sphagnum in a box.

The boxes with the Preparations 500 and 502–507 should be kept in a cool place, not in direct sunlight, and not in a refrigerator or coolstore. A suitable place would be under a house. Avoid contamination by petrol and oil fumes.

Preparation 501 is stored in a glass jar with a very loose lid in the sunlight — for example on a sunny windowsill.

## APPLICATION OF COMPOST PREPARATIONS 502–507

There are excellent descriptions of the preparations in the book *Biodynamics* prepared by the New Zealand BioDynamic Association (pp106–29), and in N Pearce (1989), *A Biodynamic Farmer's Handbook* (pp20–23).

*To compost heap*
One set of compost Preparations 502–507 is sufficient to treat up to 5 cubic metres of compost.

If you make your compost in the home garden in a bin or a small windrow-type pile which may be only 1 cubic metre in volume, you will still use one complete set.

If you make more compost, say in a long windrow-type pile 2 metres wide at the base and 1.5 metres high, you will need one set of preparations for every 5 metres of pile length. After allowing for pile shrinkage you will have approximately 1 cubic metre of compost per metre of length.

To insert Preparations 502–506, take a small handful of mature compost from a previous heap, some well-rotted cow manure, or something similar. Fold this around each preparation to make a loose ball, and insert the preparations into five holes along the side of the heap. The holes can be made with a crowbar or shovel handle.

Valerian Preparation 507 should be mixed with warmed rainwater for 10 minutes. One portion of preparation (10mls) goes into 14 litres of water, of which half is poured into two holes in the top of the heap. The remainder is sprinkled over the completed compost heap. Steiner pointed out that as soon as the preparations are inserted, the forces they carry radiate throughout the heap.

*To liquid fertilisers*
To insert the compost preparations into liquid fertilisers, put the preparations into the small amount of compost as previously described, and 'float' the compost on the top of the liquid.

The 507 can be stirred for 10 minutes in a small quantity (about 1 litre) of water, and poured into the liquid.

# Checklist for making Preparation 500

1   The cow dung for Preparation 500 should come from certified cows grazing on or fed from fodder from a biodynamic farm.
2   Avoid concentrates. The manure should be free of obvious impurities such as grass, stones, earth, bark etc.
3   The horns used must be cowhorns, not bullhorns. (Cowhorns can be distinguished from bullhorns by their annular calving rings and solid tips.)
4   The horns should be buried in soil that displays obvious biological activity. (In practice this means soil that has been regularly treated with the biodynamic preparations and biodynamic compost for at least three full years.)
5   Do not bury horns in land that becomes waterlogged.
6   The horns must be buried in the living topsoil layer, ideally at a depth of 30cm.
7   The horns must stay in the soil for at least six months, from autumn to spring, except in tropical countries.
8   The resultant Preparation 500 should have changed into a sweet-smelling, earthy, highly colloidal, reasonably firm condition.
9   The resultant Preparation 500 should also be free from impurities. Particular care should be taken when lifting, not to mix in soil or other foreign matter.
10  The preparation should be transferred immediately to storage in a cool place, in properly insulated containers. The storage area should be away from direct sunlight and free of airborne contaminants such as diesel and petrol fumes, paint flakes and so on.

# Timetable for making and applying preparations in different parts of the world

These calendars provide a rough guide for beginners. For successful bio-dynamic management, farmers need to develop a 'feel' for when is the right time to apply the preparations for their particular farm and climate.

In hot countries the fermentation time for all preparations will be shorter than in temperate climates: in warmer climates it will take 4–5 months; in cooler climates, 6–7 months.

TABLE A1: A calendar for making and using Preparation 500

| Action | NZ & temperate Australia | India, tropical Australia & Asia | Europe, northern US & Canada | California & Mediter-anean |
|---|---|---|---|---|
| Bury | April | Oct/Nov | Sept/Oct | Nov |
| Lift | late Sept | Feb/Mar | Mar/May | Mar/Apr |
| Apply[1] | | | | |
| in spring | Sept/Nov | Feb | late May/ early Jun[2] | April |
| in autumn | Mar/May | Oct/Nov[3] | Aug[4] | Oct/Nov |

1 Apply during descending moon.
2 Apply when soil temperature rises.
3 Apply after the last monsoon rains.
4 Apply before soil temperature falls.

TABLE A2: A calendar for making and using Preparations 501–508

| Prep | Year | Spring | Late spring/ summer | Autumn |
|------|------|--------|---------------------|--------|
| 501 | | bury horn | | dig up horn |
| 502 | 1 | make & hang | harvest & wilt flowers | take down & bury |
| | 2 | dig up | | |
| 503[1] | 1 | | harvest & dry flowers | make & bury |
| | 2 | dig up | | |
| 504 | 1 | | harvest foliage | bury |
| | 2 | | | dig up |
| 505 | 1 | | | gather bark, make & put in water |
| | 2 | retrieve | | |
| 506[2] | 1 | | harvest & dry flowers | make & bury |
| | 2 | dig up | | |
| 507 | | | harvest flowers & make | |
| 508 | | harvest & dry | | |

1　In most countries the flowers can be harvested and the preparation made in the late spring. Where flowers are unavailable by late spring, gather them the previous year, dry and store.
2　You could also try making it the previous spring and hanging it in a tree for 6 months, as for Preparation 502.
Note: compost, liquid manures and cowpat pit can be made, and the compost preparations added to them, at any time of the year, although decomposition is quickest during the warmer months of the year.
　　Steiner suggests hanging up the Preparations 503 and 506 (*Agriculture*, p255).

# Twenty-one points on animal health, and some remedies

1   Grow quality feed at all times, using biodynamic methods. Always have adequate reserves of fodder on hand.
2   Address mineral requirements of the soil, such as calcium and phosphate.
3   Practise good pasture management. For example, avoid overgrazing or pugging of paddocks during wet periods.
4   Avoid pasture compaction through overuse of heavy machinery which will destroy soil structure and consequently pasture quality.
5   Encourage a wide range of species of pasture plant throughout the farm (see Appendix 5). Include the deeper-rooting grasses such as cocksfoot, phalarus, prairie grass, as well as legumes such as white and red clover lucerne. Chicory is also useful.
6   Use Preparation 500 regularly, two to three times a year in spring and autumn to improve and maintain soil quality and structure.
7   Apply Preparation 501 to pasture — particularly to the hay and silage paddocks — in spring, in the morning, according to the appropriate moon rhythm to enhance fodder quality.
8   Use Preparation 502–507 regularly by means of compost, various liquid manures or cowpat pit so as to bring their influences over the whole farm. These preparations allow the energies of the planets to balance the trace elements and major nutrients, and thus give the soil the ability to grow health-giving plants. The beneficial effect on animal health of the regular and adequate use of these preparations is obvious to all biodynamic farmers.
9   Make quality silage and hay. Perfect your method. Cut your crop at the time of the appropriate moon rhythms.
10  Stock your farm at a sensible and realistic density for your area. Do not overstock.
11  Good shelter from prevailing winds will reduce stress from wind chill, and also enable better grass growth over a longer period.
12  Have good shade trees available to stock, particularly where ultraviolet light levels are high.

13  Have clean water available at all times. Take care not to have wet areas around troughs where diseases and parasites can breed.
14  Avoid other forms of stress on animals at all times. For example, take care when working animals in the yards. Avoid noisy motor-bikes and over-enthusiastic dogs.
15  Set stock on drystock units where possible, to avoid the pecking-order syndrome which arises from frequent changes of paddock.
16  Allow longer than the normally accepted times before the weaning of young stock — particularly the dairy calves or lambs you intend to keep for fattening or breeding.
17  Look to the genetic base of your animals. Some diseases are heredi-tary. Breed for health as well as for weight gain. Check that the sire with a good health record does in fact give you progeny of a good size.
18  Use herbal medicines. Strong drenches of garlic and cider vinegar are a great help with many internal parasites (see below). Use home-opathic remedies where applicable.
19  Make regular additions of herbs to fodder diet, eg rosemary, tansy, wormwood, thyme or sage. See Juliette de Baraicli Levy, *Complete Herbal Handbook for Farm and Stable* for further information.
20  Make regular additions of cider vinegar to water troughs and onto hay during the winter feeding-out time.
21  Develop the ability to be able to assess the health of your flock or herd with one glance. An early diagnosis of any problem makes for a greater chance of success with a cure.

## HERBAL DRENCHES AND TINCTURES
*Sheep drench cocktail*
The following herbal tincture, consisting of cider vinegar, fresh garlic juice, molasses and kelp, can be incorporated in animal drenches. The chemical consituents of the tincture or herbal preparation are extracted into the vinegar, which will dissolve nearly all the relevant ingredients of the herbs and at the same time act as a preservative.

To make a tincture in large quantities, use approximately 0.5–1kg of fresh herbs in a 25-litre bucket of cider vinegar. This is left to brew for at least two weeks in a warm place, and stirred daily. After decanting the bulk of the liquid, pour off the residue into a muslin cloth and wring out all the remaining liquid. The residue makes excellent compost and these tinctures will last indefinitely if stored in a dark place.

*Herbs for internal parasites*
To cleanse the body of internal parasites, use anthelmintic herbs, eg:
*Wormwood* — use the flowering tops in moderation due to its bitter taste.
The volatile oil it contains is extremely potent.
*Tansy* — use leaves and flowering tops, also in moderation as large doses
can cause abortion during pregnancy.
*Pumpkin Seed* — use ripe seeds as fresh as possible. Crush them up and
add to vinegar.
*Nasturtium* — use leaves and seeds. Nasturtium is richly medicinal as a
tonic and cleanser.
*Stinging Nettle* — use leaves and roots. This herb is rich in minerals.

*Nutritive and calmative herbs*
Tinctures can also be made from nutritive herbs such as plantain, dandelion and chickweed (use the whole plant, roots and foliage), and from
calmative herbs such as chamomile (flowering tops) and valerian (root
only), which are used to drench animals before they are transported to
the abattoir.

*Drench to combat lice*
Sulphur can be made up to a 12D potency as a means of combating lice
in stock. The sulphur is dynamised with lactose, as this makes the sulphur water-soluble. A few drops are put into the sheep drench and also
into the cattle water-trough.

The cattle will drink the natural drench from the trough, although it
is best to orally drench young cattle so they get a taste for it. Stock are
brought into the yards to fast overnight before drenching. Water with
potentised sulphur added is available at all times. The animals are
drenched in the morning (lambs 10ml twice daily; sheep 20ml twice daily;
young cattle 100ml twice daily), left for 3–4 hours, then drenched again in
the afternoon before returning to pasture.

*Stress in stock*
Since the animals are drenched fortnightly from a young age, they
become used to the process. They are less stressed by it, are easier to
muster and handle, and generally more responsive to humans. In time,
all stock can be trained to take the drench from troughs.

Roxanne Gilbert
Sheep farmer
Dannevirke, NZ

## APPENDIX FIVE

# A herbal ley seed mixture

Note: this mixture was developed by Grasslands, DSIR (now AgResearch) for New Zealand conditions (ie a temperate climate). Consult local agronomists for other species which will grow well in your district.

This mixture contains legumes for nitrogen fixation; many deep-rooted species which tolerate drought, increase soil porosity, and access more minerals; several herbs with high mineral content; and species which give a low risk of sheep facial eczema. Not all species will grow in all districts. Sow in early autumn or early spring.

Recommended sowing rate is 11.5kg (25lb) per acre. The species in the mixture are in approximate balance on a seed-weight basis.

1  *Chicory* — 'Puna': a persistent deep tap-rooted pasture herb which is high-producing, high in minerals and has high-quality summer forage. Excellent animal performance has been recorded with this species. It is suited to free-draining soils.

2  *Yarrow* — a mineral-rich forage herb, persistent, with an extensive rhizome system.

3  *Sheep's Burnet* — a fast-establishing perennial herb producing palatable summer forage. Performs well in dry, low-fertility sites and withstands cold winters.

4  *Plantain* — narrow-leaf plantain: deep-rooted summer-growing herb.

5  *Trefoil* — a deep-rooted legume, non-bloating, excellent summer growth, particularly suited to dry, acid, low-fertility soils.

6  *Lucerne* — 'Oranga': deep tap-rooted legume, very drought-tolerant, producing quality summer forage.

7  *Sulla* — 'Aokau': short-lived perennial legume, rapid establishment, very productive during winter. Produces non-bloating forage.

8  *Subterranean Clover* — an annual legume, low-growing, with excellent winter growth, able to persist through vigorous reseeding, thus surviving dry summers.

9    *Pink Serradella* — 'Koha': a deep-rooted winter annual legume, tolerant of acid soils.

10   *White Clover* — 'Pitau': a persistent legume adapted to a wide range of environments. Creeping, prostrate habit with a network of spreading stolons.

11   *Red Clover* — 'Pawera' and 'Hamua': a tap-rooted perennial legume. Produces high-quality summer forage and is drought-tolerant. Early and late flowering types combined.

12   *Prairie Grass* — 'Matua': a perennial grass with a good winter growth. Best suited to higher-fertility soils that are free-draining. Grows well during winter and dry summers.

13   *Yorkshire Fog* — 'Massey Basin': a perennial grass, very palatable. Grows well on low-fertility and acid soils.

14   *Browntop* — 'Muster': pasture browntop suitable for low-fertility and acid soils. A perennial grass with a dense rhizomatous growth habit.

15   *Hybrid Ryegrass* — 'Greenstone': a persistent tetraploid hybrid ryegrass, very palatable. No endophyte, giving excellent winter/spring growth. Tillers strongly.

16   *Cocksfoot* — 'Wana': a perennial ryegrass with a deep root-system, well adapted to dry, low-fertility soils. Active over the summer.

17   *Phalarus* — 'Maru': perennial grass with active cool-season growth. Tolerant of dry, harsh environments and of insect pests, including grass-grub.

18   *Timothy* — 'Kahu': high forage-quality grass, especially good on moist sites.

# Conversion from metric to approximate British equivalents

*Square measure*
1 hectare = 2.471 acres

*Cubic measure*
1 cubic metre = 1.308 cu. yards

*Capacity measure*
1 millilitre = 0.002 pint (British)
1 litre = 1.76 pints
10 litres = 2.20 gallons

*Weight*
1 kilogram = 2.205 pounds
1 tonne (1000 kg) = 0.984 (long) ton

Source: *The Concise Oxford Dictionary*, 8th edn, 1990.

APPENDIX SEVEN

# Biodynamic associations — contact details

Biodynamic associations throughout the world provide some or all of the following services for their members:
- information and advice
- sale of preparations
- directories of suppliers for various resources
- farm inspection and certification to Demeter standards
- educational seminars, discussion groups, courses in biodynamic methods

**New Zealand**

The Bio Dynamic Farming and Gardening Association in New Zealand (Inc.) PO Box 39045, Wellington Mail Centre, New Zealand.
Ph +64 4 589 5366
e-mail biodynamics@clear.net.nz

**Australia**

The Biodynamic Farming and Gardening Association in Australia (Inc.)
PO Box 54, Bellingen, NSW 2454, Australia.
Ph +61 2 6655 8551
e-mail poss@midcoast.com.au

**USA**

Biodynamic Farming and Gardening Association (Inc.) Building 1002B, Thoreau Centre, The Presidio, PO Box 29135, San Francisco, CA 94129 0135.
Ph +1 415 561 7797
e-mail biodynamic@aol.com

**Canada**

Bio-Dynamic Agricultural Society of British Columbia, Skimikin Road, CDN-Chase, BC VOE 1MO,
ph +1 604 679 8052, fax +1 604 679 2932

**Hawaii**

Biodynamics Hawaii. 2514 Alaula Way, Honolulu, HI 96822, Hawaii, USA.
Ph +1 808 988 4555
e-mail pdwyer@hawaii.rr.com

**United Kingdom**

Biodynamic Agricultural Association, Painswick Inn, Gloucester Street, Stroud, Gloucestershire GL5 1QG, UK.
Ph +44 145 375 9501
e-mail bdaa@biodynamic.freeserve.co.uk

**India**

Bio Dynamic Association of India, No 78, 1$^{st}$ Floor, 11$^{th}$ Cross, Indiranagar 1$^{st}$ Stage, Bangalore, Karnataka, India.
Ph +91 80 5272 185
e-mail imoind@blr.vsnl.net.in

**Germany**

Forschungsring für biol.-dyn. Wirtschaftsweise, Brandschneise 2, D-64295 Darmstadt
Ph +49 (06155) 84690, fax +49 (06155) 846 911
e-mail demeterbd@-online.de

**Ireland**

Bio-Dynamic Agricultural Association in Ireland, Ballinroan House, IRL-Kiltegan, Co. Wicklow, fax +353 508 81006

**South Africa**

Bio-Dynamic Agricultural Association of Southern Africa, PO Box 115, Paulshof, South Africa 2056, ph +27 11 803 1688

There are also associations in Quebec and Ontario in Canada, and in Austria, Brazil, Denmark, Finland, France, Israel, Italy, Croatia, Luxembourg, Netherlands, Norway, Sweden, Switzerland, Slovenia and Spain.

# Bibliography

Baraicli Levy, Juliette de, 1976. *Complete Herbal Handbook for Farm and Stable*, Rodale Press, Emmaus, PA.

BioDynamic Farming & Gardening Association in New Zealand, published annually. *BioDynamic Farming and Gardening Calendar*, Napier.

Bockemuhl, Jochen, 1981, *In Partnership with Nature*, Bio-Dynamic Literature, Wyoming, RI.

Carter, Neil, 1989. 'Some new research aspects of biodynamics', in *Biodynamics — New Directions for Farming and Gardening in New Zealand*, Random Century NZ, Auckland.

Grohmann, G, 1974. *The Plant*, 2 vols, Rudolf Steiner Press, London.

Koenig, K, 1982. *Earth and Man*, Biodynamic Literature, Wyoming.

Koepf, Herbert H, 1987. *The Biodynamic Farm: Agriculture in Service of the Earth and Humanity*, Anthroposophic Press, Bells Pond, NY.

Leivegoed, BCJ, 1951. *The Workings of the Planets and Life Processes in Man and Earth*, Experimental Circle of Anthroposophical Farmers & Gardeners, Clent.

Kolisko, Eugen & Lilli, 1978. *Agriculture of Tomorrow*, Kolisko Archive Publications, Bournemouth.

MacGregor, AN, 1996, pers. communication.

Mortimer, John & Bunny, 1984. *Trees for the New Zealand Countryside*, Silverfish, Auckland.

Pearce, Norrie, 1989. *A Biodynamic Farmer's Handbook*, AN Pearce, PO Box 26295, Epsom, Auckland.

Pfeiffer, Ehrenfried, 1983. *Soil Fertility, Renewal and Preservation*, Lanthorn Press, East Grinstead.

Pfeiffer, Ehrenfried, 1960. 'Chromatography applied to quality testing', Biodynamic Farming & Gardening Association, Stroudsberg, PA.

Reganold, John P, AS Palmer, JC Lockhart & AN Macgregor, 1993. 'Soil quality and financial performance of biodynamic and conventional farms in New Zealand', *Science* 260, 16 April.

Schwenk, Theodor, 1965. *Sensitive Chaos: The Creation of Flowing Forms in Water and Air*, Rudolf Steiner Press, London.

Steiner, Rudolf, 1970. *Man as Symphony of the Creative Word*, Rudolf Steiner Press, London.

Steiner, Rudolf, 1993. *Agriculture*, trans. CE Creeger & M Gardner, Bio-Dynamic Farming & Gardening Association, Kimberton, PA.

Thun, Maria, 1979. *Working on the Land and the Constellations*, Lanthorn Press, East Grinstead.

Van Stensil, 1994, pers. communication.

Wachsmuth, Guenther, 1932. *The Etheric Formative Forces*, Anthroposophical Publishing, London.

Willis, Harold, 1985. *The Coming Revolution in Agriculture*, A.R. Editions, Wisconsin.

## A seminar at Kurinji

Beneath the canopy of palm and neem
a new-made meeting hall was to be seen
Roof of coconut fragrant to most
with low rock walls and granite post

Mango and lime are at their peak
with wattle, mahogany, rosewood and teak.
All makes for pleasant cooling shade
to listen to farming plans well laid.
Rice-flour patterns at entrance welcome
A snake slithers to its home garden.

Eighty farmers and wives in white
waiting to hear the message right
Of cowhorns, compost and silica pure
and structured humus and cow manure.
Bananas, pineapples they grow,
cashews, coffee and some NGOs

Kurinji has with very much care
prepared a seminar that all can share
Liquid made and compost too
and horns are filled with dung so new
and also the BD orchard to view.

Many's the doubt that needs to be answered
of this direction to be mastered
But this courage now to change the way
and let 500 compost rule the day.

— Peter Proctor

# Index